The
Scenic
Route

The Scenic Route

A Way through Madness

ROSSA FORBES

INSPIRED CREATIONS LLC

To find out more about the author, visit rossaforbes.com

Edited by JT Hinds, theimpeccableeditor.com

Cover design by Cléa Lautry, clealautry.com

Why does anybody tell a story? It does indeed have something to do with faith, faith that the universe has meaning, that our little human lives are not irrelevant, that what we choose or say or do matters, matters cosmically.

— Madeleine L'Engle

CONTENTS

ACKNOWLEDGMENTS

This story would have been impossible to tell without the loving understanding and support of my son, Chris.

I am grateful to my husband and to Chris's younger brothers for their steadfast commitment to our family. Thank you to the many people in our small community who have acted as Chris's spiritual guides, life coaches, and friends in need, and to the online community of survivors who informed my thinking.

I owe a big debt of gratitude to my editor, JT Hinds, who patiently and persistently showed me how to improve as writer.

AUTHOR'S NOTE

Many in today's recovery movement (including me) question the value of using terms such as *schizophrenia, mental illness,* and even *recovery.* As these terms are familiar to the general public, I have opted, in the interests of clarity and efficiency, not to create confusion by adopting new terminology.

Angela Blaen, PhD, Pier Rubesa, researcher and inventor, and Pastor Bill Strehlow have kindly given me permission to use their names. The names of health care professionals and family members have been changed to protect their privacy.

Doctors Vandemaele, Tissot, and Blancpain are composite characters based upon the many doctors who evaluated and treated my son while he was an inpatient (at the Centre for Addiction and Mental Health and the Hôpital de psychiatrie de Belle-Idée) and a day patient (in the early psychosis program at the Hôpitaux Universitaires de Genève).

Chapter 1

☀ *Cosmic Concerns*

IN SEPTEMBER 2002, on the morning Chris was due to leave home to begin life as an undergraduate at Trinity College, University of Toronto, he still had not packed his bags. Clothes were strewn all over his bedroom; his suitcases were empty. He sat on the edge of his bed, dazed.

"Get packing," I yelled. "The taxi is arriving in half an hour!"

Chris remained motionless, so I threw all of his clothes and necessities into two suitcases and slammed them shut, wondering how he was going to survive on his own if he couldn't even pack a suitcase.

Half an hour later, I watched from the window as Chris and his father loaded the luggage into the taxi and headed for the airport to catch their flight. Tears rolled down my cheeks. Something was terribly wrong. My firstborn had gone from being a dedicated, organized, and intellectually ambitious student to a confused young man who needed constant prodding to complete his work.

What happened? I wondered. In his last year of high school, my son had lost his edge. His final exam results in the International Baccalaureate (IB) program at the International School of Geneva had fallen short of his teachers' (and his parents') expectations.

We'd had a crazy and exhausting year. My husband and I had gotten far too caught up in the college application process, endlessly discussing with Chris the merits of one university over another. Chris had applied to a number of top-notch schools in Europe and North America and had been accepted into most of them. He had his heart set on going to a particular Ivy League school—and got in—but, financially, it was too much of a stretch for us. (We thought a broader, more egalitarian experience could be obtained at a good public university. Save the Ivies for graduate school, we reasoned.)

Chris wasn't enthusiastic about any of the other universities. Ian and I convinced him that Trinity was his best option. Academically, the University of Toronto was one of the most highly ranked schools in Canada, we pointed out. In Toronto, he would be close to extended family that he could visit on breaks or call on in an emergency.

My son's lack of enthusiasm concerned me. Did it stem from ambivalence, I wondered, or apathy? *Apathy* describes a lack of interest or energy and an unwillingness to take action, even over an important matter. *Ambivalence* describes uncertainty and is characterized by contradictory feelings.

I turned away from the window, recalling the events of the past year that had caused me so much worry. Chris didn't just have a bad case of senioritis, as I'd initially thought.

The autumn of Chris's last year of high school seemed particularly gloomy, even for Geneva. The chill Bise came whistling through every nook and cranny of our apartment, making the tea lights on our dinner table flicker like votive candles. I gamely tried to keep dinner conversation going, but eventually gave up. Chris sat silently with his hands in his lap, his head bowed, as if in silent prayer. Alex and Taylor, his younger brothers, were subdued, and my husband, Ian, was more intent on eating than talking. Sometimes when I spoke, Chris looked up in my direction and put his fingers to his lips to hush me. The tea lights were a mistake, I reckoned; they only emphasized the gloom.

Chris had applied to Cambridge University for a place in chemistry and was granted an interview. In early December, I flew with him to

England, but the interview didn't go well. Chris wasn't particularly interested in career paths like engineering, computer science, or medicine. He had done well in math and chemistry, but his scholarly leanings were more theoretical than practical. (His chemistry teacher once told me he'd make an excellent theoretical chemist.)

In his application to Cambridge, Chris had expressed a vague interest in studying the essence of matter. I considered that a tad presumptuous and a bit strange—more like the musings of an ancient alchemist than a modern chemist. Had I known more at that time about alchemy, I might have realized that Chris's interests held clues that he was about to set foot on a spiritual path.[1]

The interview didn't go well. The interviewer said that Chris lacked confidence. I had noticed that his enthusiasm and energy had been waning over the past few months, but I couldn't attribute the change to anything other than the academic stresses of the final year of school.

Then came the head tapping.

The day after the interview, we took the one-and-a-half-hour flight from Luton back to Geneva. Chris sat next to me, in the window seat. The plane was within inches of touching down when I was jolted out of my reading.

"Yeow!"

I turned to see Chris's hand shooting to his temple. He looked shocked. The plane landed, and the pain disappeared as suddenly as it had started.

Having brought only carry-on luggage, we went immediately to the first aid office at the airport after clearing immigration. The nurse shrugged. "Un mystère," she said.

The next day, Chris visited our family doctor and explained what had happened. "Nothing to worry about," the doctor assured him. A follow-up visit revealed no new information.

The doctor didn't suspect a problem, but over the next few months Chris kept tapping a certain spot on his temple, saying it felt like an indentation. Taylor, who was thirteen at the time, cheerfully weighed in with his opinion: "If it were a tumor, it would be pushing out." Chris went back to the doctor and received the same answer as before. I tried not to worry. Our family doctor wasn't concerned enough to order tests, I told myself. But I *was* worried.

What the doctor didn't pick up on, and neither did I, was a possible problem with Chris's prefrontal cortex, the part of the brain that gives us the capacity to set goals and take purposeful actions to achieve them.[2] Without the ability to plan for the future, Chris would find it difficult to acquire the life skills necessary for functioning as an independent adult.

By the time spring examinations rolled around, Chris had stopped tapping on his head. The photograph of his graduating class, taken earlier in the year, shows a strained-looking young man sitting far away from his friends. Leaning forward on his elbows, his hands were crisscrossed in an odd gesture; the middle finger of each hand was braided around the ring finger, sending a coded message to the sleeping world.

Several days after Chris's graduation, our family went to see *A Beautiful Mind*, the film about Nobel laureate John Nash's descent into madness, at our local theater. (Everyone but Alex, our sixteen-year-old, who, with school out for the summer, slept most days and partied with his friends most nights.) Ian was particularly interested in seeing the film because he had once heard Nash speak at an American Economic Association convention.[3]

I knew nothing about schizophrenia (so I was surprised when Nash's college roommate turned out to be a hallucination), but I left the theater with an undefined worry about Chris.

Taylor identified it. "Ha, he was tapping his head just like Chris did."

At the time, I didn't make a conscious connection between John Nash's symptoms and Chris's symptoms. I wasn't familiar with psychosis or primed to look for it, so I had earlier that year missed such subtleties as Chris putting his fingers to his lips to keep his mother quiet at the dinner table so that the pope could get a word in. (The pope first spoke to Chris during a church service, Chris revealed to me several years later. "The pope of all people, Chris? We're not even Catholic!" I joked.)

Chapter 2

✳ Ophelia

A WEEK AFTER SEEING *A Beautiful Mind*, I overheard Chris and Ian talking in low voices in Chris's bedroom. I crept to the closed door and listened. "Ophelia is a lovely girl," I heard Ian say.

I had a sense of foreboding—with good reason, as it turned out. I gathered from the conversation that Chris wanted to marry Ophelia, a classmate of his who was also the daughter of a friend of mine. Chris was unsure what to do because Ophelia was leaving for university in London in a few months—this was unbearable for him. He didn't want to go to Toronto; he wanted to find a job in Geneva to support Ophelia. In his mind, going to university was nowhere in the picture.

Marry Ophelia? This plan was well beyond strange. To my knowledge, Chris and Ophelia hadn't even been dating! I reminded myself that young people fall in love all the time, but I knew that where Chris was concerned, something else was going on. There had been no lead-up to this sudden, earth-shattering declaration. Ian was as shocked as I was.

I spent much of the weekend lying on my bed staring at the ceiling. On Monday, I went to my weekly lunch with Irene, and I mentioned that Chris was seeing her daughter. Irene quickly let me know that Ophelia thought of Chris as a dear friend only.

I came home wondering how Chris could make the leap to marriage when his relationship with Ophelia was so one-sided. There was nothing solid enough about it to justify forgoing university. Irene had confided to me during our lunch that she had recently learned that Chris's friends had been worried about him.

Worried about him? I felt sick. What had they noticed? Why hadn't one of them said something to me? I quickly realized that wasn't really their responsibility. I, too, had noticed how withdrawn Chris had become over the course of the year. When his friends came over, Chris was unusually quiet. The others would be chatting and laughing, but not Chris. He didn't seem depressed, but he didn't smile much either.

Other changes had crept into his behavior, and even his appearance seemed different. His face had always been pale, but now his skin had a waxy look. He spoke in a halting monotone, which made him sound mechanical. His conversation was devoid of interesting observations. He once went on, in mind-numbing detail, about the chemical makeup of the soft drink he was sipping.

I recalled other worrisome instances when friends of the family had telephoned and Chris answered the phone; there wasn't the usual warmth of recognition in his voice. He acted as if he had never met these people—and didn't want to!

For the next two weeks, Chris took the train to Ophelia's house most afternoons, returning home in time for dinner. Would he propose marriage? Ian and I both wondered. The unexpectedness and the depth of his life-altering plan scared me. He was clearly wearing his heart on his sleeve. This wasn't the Chris-in-love that I would have expected, if the path of love is predictable at all.

"Why not take Chris to China with you?" I asked my husband one day. Ian was travelling to Beijing for work the following week and had air miles to spare.

He embraced the idea enthusiastically. "You're brilliant!" he said. "Chris will be distracted by the new and strange. After ten days without Ophelia, the situation will have resolved itself somehow, and Chris will be that much closer to starting university."

Life would move on.

Alas, the trip to Beijing did not go well, according to Ian. Chris took no interest in the extra two days of sightseeing that Ian had scheduled, choosing to sit in the tour bus while the rest of the group visited an acupuncture center. Ian was frustrated. He and Chris quarreled a lot, which was something new in their relationship.

"But, he amazed me," said my husband. "When we were at the Summer Palace, we met an Australian woman who was in a panic because she had lost sight of her husband half an hour before, and the stream of tourists was so deep and fast-moving that she didn't know if he was ahead of her or behind her. Chris told her he was sure he'd passed the man and would go find him. Then he quickly walked back the way we'd come—and returned with the woman's husband! How did he know where this man was, or who he was? It was strange."

("I observe everything," Chris told me years later. "I sensed the direction of the wind and where the moss grew on the walls. I knew I would find him," he said with quiet confidence.)

Chapter 3

Grandiose Ideas ✳

CHRIS'S LOVE FOR OPHELIA seemed to have run its course in the time he was away, as he no longer took the train to see her after he returned from the China trip. Ian and I didn't discuss Ophelia with Chris; we concentrated on helping him prepare for his upcoming move to Toronto—despite his lack of enthusiasm or effort. We worried that he was about to ruin his first year of university, which hadn't even started.

Based on his IB results, Chris was eligible to claim college credits for first-year biology, chemistry, and math, allowing him to enroll in advanced courses in those subjects. Ian and I had both attended schools in Canada; we warned Chris that an IB course was not the equivalent of a course at a competitive college. Entering a second-year math or science course without having completed the first-year prerequisite would be a risky undertaking.

Chris was determined to claim first-year credits, so we suggested, in the spirit of compromise, that he only claim credit for a course if he was planning not to pursue that subject area further. He agreed to our suggestion.

He also wanted to take a first-year physics course, despite the fact that he had not taken physics in his last two years of high school. "This can be done," the admissions official informed him, "as long as a student is good in math and is willing to work."

"Okay, if you insist," Ian and I said to Chris, "but whatever you do, do NOT claim credit for first-year math. You'll find a first-year math course challenging enough."

I had the sinking feeling that even that advice wouldn't stick. It would have been far easier for all of us if Chris had taken these kinds of risks as a child, when the stakes were low and he had plenty of time to learn from his failures. Flaming out at university would be an expensive way to experience failure.

The expression "bigger children, bigger problems" was starting to hit home.

As Chris's departure date drew closer, he approached Ian and me with a new idea.

"There's really no point in my going to Toronto before classes start. I already know what courses I'll be taking, so why should I bother with orientation week?"

Ian and I were dumbfounded. *Everybody* goes to orientation week. How could Chris possibly think about skipping it?

We tried talking some sense into him. He would have an opportunity to make new friends and get familiar with the campus, we felt compelled to point out. "You're not so sophisticated, Chris, that you couldn't benefit from the academic advice that's available, in addition to the parties and the beer."

Chris seemed to think that his mind was far more capable than the minds of mere mortals. He already knew everything he needed to know. He didn't have to go through the steps like everyone else.

Ian and I were beginning to see a pattern. A couple of months earlier, Chris had enrolled in a driving school. As part of the program, students could attend a practice session at a driving range when they were close to taking their driver's test. Chris decided to go to the driving range midway through his course. An irate instructor ordered him to go home and come back when he was ready.

Ian and I were as astounded then as we were now. "What were you thinking, Chris?" we chimed. "Did you actually think you know everything there is to know about driving?"

The possibility that such cocksure behavior might be a sign of mental illness didn't occur to us. My experience in raising three sons and entertaining their male friends had taught me that they all have an inflated sense of their own skills, especially where sports prowess and vehicles are concerned. They brag about their plans to ski the black diamond runs, even if they are novices. They all seem to think they'll get their driver's licenses in a matter of days and that they'll pass the test on the first try. We hoped Chris was just demonstrating that kind of bravado. Maybe his overconfidence was even a good sign.

If Chris weren't normally so self-effacing, this particular trait (psychiatrists call it "grandiosity") could well have remained hidden. He had always been so compliant, a follower of the rules. If I was witnessing an emerging rebel, I took comfort in the hope that he was finally attempting to chart his own course.

Had we known the depth of Chris's problems, Ian and I might have taken his reluctance to go to university at face value, put aside our plans, and encouraged him to stay home. As it was, the momentum of our parental expectations was far too great for us to stop and think about what might really be happening. Chris's place at the University of Toronto had been secured; the airplane tickets had been purchased. It was too late to turn back.

Chapter 4

✳ *The Hero's Journey*

DESPITE HIS INITIAL RELUCTANCE, Chris attended orientation week and enjoyed himself. From the phone calls and letters Ian and I received over the next few weeks, we could tell that he was having fun and taking advantage of campus life, and we were cautiously optimistic that he would settle into his courses.

One afternoon, when I was in the middle of tidying up Chris's room, the phone rang.

"Mom, I want to get credit for my IB math course and go into second-year math," Chris said. "This course is too easy. I've covered most of the work already."

My heart sank. This could only spell trouble. However, I was fed up with Chris's unusual attitude in the face of common sense.

"Do what you want," I snapped. "It's your life."

I hung up the phone and returned to cleaning, thinking of Chris's puzzling behavior with every photo and school paper and scrap of his recent life that I uncovered.

Why didn't he just go ahead and sign up for the second-year course if he was so determined? Chris not only asked for permission about matters he should be deciding for himself, he apologized for even the slightest missteps. I used to joke that even as a toddler Chris asked for permission to breathe the air. He studiously avoided misbehavior and was averse to taking risks, so apologies were unnecessary. My constant encouragement to stop asking permission all the time had produced no change in his behavior in the eighteen years he had been on earth. He'd been hesitant from the start.

Chris had been conceived on April 8, 1983, in Ottawa, Canada, where Ian and I were living at the time. I remember the exact date because I actually heard a vibrating, pinging sound when sperm met egg. A subsequent ultrasound set the due date as December 19, exactly forty weeks to the day. No surprise there.

After that initial *ping*, Chris did little to make his presence known. Throughout my lengthy pregnancy, he hardly ever kicked or moved. (I knew he was a boy. Mother's intuition . . .)

"Lots of movement?" Doctor Lee always asked during his monthly prodding of my belly.

What should I tell him?

Chris was my first. The ultrasounds didn't indicate any problems. I wasn't having any health issues related to the pregnancy. If I told the doctor I didn't feel a lot of movement, I knew I would probably be given all kinds of invasive tests that would prove nothing. I decided to just nod my head and agree, thinking, *This baby is never gonna be a hockey player.*

December 19 came and went.

"Do you want to be induced?" Doctor Lee asked during my next visit to his office.

"No, let's just wait and see what happens," I said. "He'll come when he's ready."

I now made weekly visits to the hospital for an electronic fetal monitoring test. I was given orange juice to drink to stimulate fetal movement. Despite the baby being well overdue, the tests showed there was no cause for alarm.

"Be prepared for a girl," the technician said during one of my visits. "High heartbeat."

"No," I said confidently, "it's a boy."

The days and weeks dragged on. Finally, in the early hours of January 15, 1984, my contractions started. Ian and I headed to the hospital.

The next twenty-four hours were rough. Twenty-seven days past his due date, Chris still wasn't in any rush. I initially refused the epidural that was offered, but eventually, too exhausted to hold out any longer, I jettisoned the idea of natural childbirth. The epidural, however, slowed the birth process.

"Be prepared for a girl," the nurse in the delivery room warned as she removed the fetal monitor, echoing the technician's earlier prediction. "I'm registering a high heartbeat."

"No, it's a boy," I said.

"Seven pounds nine ounces and all ten fingers and toes," Doctor Lee crowed as he handed me my bundle of joy. "I had to use forceps," he said, "but his test scores are healthy—and here's the proof that his ultrasound due date was accurate. His fingers are peeling from being so overdue."

I gazed at my newborn and thought, *What beautiful red lips.*

My thoughts turned from reminiscing about Chris's birth to the messy reality of his room. He used to be pretty neat and tidy, I recalled; up until the previous year, I'd never had to nag him about cleaning.

Strewn throughout the clutter were assorted pieces of paper. When I picked one up, I saw Ophelia's name and address, in Chris's handwriting, at the top of the page.

It was a strange love poem and reminded me of something a medieval troubadour might pen for a lady. The poet spoke of testing his strength, as if he were planning to undertake a series of extraordinary challenges in order to win the love of his intended.

Despite my unease about Chris's state of mind, I reasoned that the words were no more bizarre than the lyrics of many songs. Chris was a keen musician—he'd been playing the guitar since he was thirteen—so it all kind of made sense.

The poem was beautiful and oddly meaningful. I was impressed by the feeling, the striving, and the idealism it conveyed.

I kept the poem and tore up the other papers, hoping that the confusion that had inspired Chris's outpouring was gone.

At the time, I hadn't heard of mythologist Joseph Campbell, author of *The Hero with a Thousand Faces*, who noted that all great myths describe, to some extent, the same "hero's journey."[1] The hero, living in ordinary circumstances, receives a call (hearing, perhaps, a voice) that catapults him into the land of the supernatural. He endures many tests and hardships, possibly even suffering spiritual death in order to be resurrected. As a result of this ordeal, he gains special knowledge that he may choose to share with others if he accepts the challenge of returning to his native land. The journey home is fraught with peril too, but the gift the hero brings back will somehow enrich the world.

Broadly speaking, the ancient mythical hero was physically robust, action-oriented, and recognized for his work—much like the war heroes that nations continue to honor with medals. Campbell, who was influenced by early twentieth-century theorists Carl Jung, Sigmund Freud, and Arnold van Gennep, identified a new and different kind of hero in *The Hero with a Thousand Faces*.

The hero of our time, according to Campbell, is internally focused, unsure of himself and his place in the world, and is often misunderstood. His challenges are psychic ones. He intuits relational meaning (synchronicities) from the "timeless universe of symbols."[2] People who can interpret these symbols (prophets, priests, and shamans) held a higher status in traditional cultures than they do in the modern world, which revolves around materialism rather than symbolism.

In 1968, Campbell received a letter from Jungian psychiatrist John Weir Perry, MD, along with a reprint of a paper on schizophrenia that Doctor Perry had written in 1962. From Perry's paper, Campbell learned that the imagery of schizophrenic fantasy matched that of the mythological hero journey that he had outlined years before in *The Hero with a Thousand Faces*.[3]

Both Campbell and Jung describe the hero's journey as a descent experience, a dark night of the soul. In Christian theology, the dark night of the soul is illuminated by an ever-present light. The light leads the hero to self-knowledge and, ultimately, to union with the divine. Sometimes the hero is accompanied on his journey by someone who undergoes a parallel experience. In time, I would consider myself privileged to share Chris's journey and to discover that psychiatric illness could be a stimulus for growth—his and mine.

But before growth could happen, we first had to descend into the abyss.

Chapter 5

A Painful Truth ✳

CHRIS RETURNED FROM his first year at the University of
Toronto on academic probation. He had failed physics and second-
year math. He'd scraped by in first-year chemistry and a second-year
literary criticism course, and he got a decent grade in his humanities
course, "Making Sense of Myth."

Chris was nonchalant about his dismal academic performance. Just
about everyone he knew at Trinity had failed a course or two, he said. They
were all planning to redeem themselves the following year, apparently.

Ian and I were exasperated. This behavior was so unlike the
good ole reliable Chris we used to know, and yet we still couldn't
help thinking that maybe this was his long overdue rebellion. During
his time in the womb and throughout his childhood he'd been
unwilling—or unable—to rock the boat.

Chris's newly grown black beard stood out in shocking contrast
to his pale skin and blond hair. The beard was long and unkempt, not
the fresh-out-of-bed-but-still-well-groomed look that was popular
at the time. Kudos to him for wanting to make a statement, Ian and
I agreed, but we worried about the message he was sending. He was

beginning to look like a locust eater, a modern-day John the Baptist.

One day, shortly after he arrived home for the summer, I asked Chris to find some cord so we could tie the potted trees on our balcony to the railing to prevent them from blowing over. He bought some heavy cord from the local hardware store and then deliberated about how he should go about accomplishing the task. Rather than just winching the rope around the tree and tying it to the balcony railing, he constructed a labyrinthine looping system that looked like a spider web.

"I think of it as rather John Nashian," Chris declared, standing back to admire his work.

What is he going on about? I wondered. *Why doesn't he just tie the rope from the tree to the railing? What's John Nash got to do with this? Just keep it simple, Chris; stop trying to impress us with your metaphors,* I fumed to myself.

Now, along with the John-the-Baptist look, Chris's appearance was beginning to look nerdish. He was buttoning his shirt all the way up (including the top button) and tucking his shirt into his pants, belt riding high. His gait was different too. There used to be a natural rhythm in his walk. Now, his posture was slumped and one foot turned in slightly.

"Chris, unbutton the top button of your shirt," I scolded. "Don't tuck everything in. Stand up straight. You're nineteen, not forty-nine!"

The change in him was heartbreaking to see.

Occasionally, Chris sat down at the piano and played—on and on. He created beautiful, sensitive, imaginative music that was totally his own. It dawned on me that he had spent a lot of time playing the piano at Trinity, but doing little else. Certainly not studying.

Later that summer, Taylor observed that Chris had been burning through complex novels at the rate of one a day. Just to verify that Chris had actually retained what he'd read, Taylor would open a book, choose a random passage, and ask Chris what it was about. Chris had no difficulty recalling the passage in detail.

Two weeks before Chris was due back at Trinity to begin his second year, I woke up early one morning and headed to the kitchen for a glass of water. I looked in on Chris. He wasn't in his room, nor was he in the apartment. It was 4:00 a.m.

I sat in the darkened living room, unsure what to do, until I heard a noise in the outside hallway. I unlocked the door.

"Chris?" I called softly.

I barely got a glimpse of him as he yanked open the door to the stairwell and bolted down the stairs like a frightened animal. I decided to wait in the living room until he returned. Twenty minutes later, his key turned in the lock.

"Where were you?" I asked. "Why did you run off?"

"Oh, I was just being silly," he said sheepishly, avoiding my gaze. "Sorry for worrying you." He went straight to his room and closed the door.

I was grateful he'd returned safely—and I realized that when he was away at school I wasn't privy to his every movement—but his answer did nothing to ease my worried mind.

I went back to bed but didn't sleep a wink.

The next day Chris and I had a little talk. We'd been having a lot of these little talks lately.

"Where did you go last night?" I asked.

"Oh, just for a walk around the park."

"At four o'clock in the morning? Why would you go to the park?"

"I wanted to get beaten up."

It was with this horrific confession, spoken ever so mildly and matter-of-factly, that the state of Chris's mental health finally got through to me. He needed professional help. This wasn't a normal phase of development. It was something truly dark and frightening.

In the morning, I went to my office, but I was unable to keep my mind on my work. I spoke with a colleague, who recommended Damien Piaget, a psychologist in the area who worked with children and adolescents. I called Doctor Piaget in a state of panic. I told him that my husband and I were worried about our teenage son, who had begun acting very strangely. He agreed to see Chris later that week. Ian and I would see him the day after Chris's appointment.

At home that evening, Ian and I explained to Chris that we were worried about him and wanted him to talk to a psychologist. Chris stared at us, expressionless; he didn't object or refuse, just shrugged his shoulders and quietly said, "Okay."

On the day of Chris's appointment, I got up as usual to put coffee on. As I gazed out onto the balcony, I spotted something at the base of the potted tree. Stepping outside for a closer look, I saw that it was a turd—a solid chunk of human excrement.

"Chris, what is this thing at the bottom of the tree?" I called out.

"What do you think it is!" he yelled from his bedroom, in an irritated tone of voice (as if a human turd in a planter were a normal occurrence).

"Well . . . dispose of it!" I yelled back.

My mind reeled with an image of Chris, luminously white and naked in the moonlight, backing himself into the planter, oblivious as to who might be watching.

Chris returned home from his late afternoon session with Damien Piaget, reporting that he "seemed to be a nice fellow," but revealing little else before retreating to the bathroom and locking the door.

The next evening, Ian and I sat stiffly in Doctor Piaget's waiting room, mindful of the *tick tick tick*ing of the clock on the wall. Right on time, Doctor Piaget emerged from his office to greet us as his previous clients scuttled anonymously through a side exit. We shook hands all around and followed the psychologist into his office.

"I'm glad you're here," he said as Ian and I settled into our chairs. "There's a lot going on with Chris right now. He seems to have an intense fantasy life, but he doesn't strike me as depressed."

Doctor Piaget asked if anyone in Ian's or my family had experienced similar problems around Chris's age.

Ian and I weren't sure what he was looking for but offered that Ian's sister had been anorexic, my sister dyslexic, and Ian mildly obsessive-compulsive. Ian's mother had suffered from depression when she was in her thirties and had undergone electroshock treatments. Doctor Piaget didn't seem to find any of these revelations important.

"Does he . . . ? You know," asked Doctor Piaget, making a quick hand gesture that signified masturbation. Ian and I looked at each other, not having the remotest idea.

We discussed the turd incident, and we told Doctor Piaget about Ophelia. He then used a word I hadn't heard before: decompensating. In his opinion, a romantic relationship would be disastrous for Chris. I felt both indignant and sad on Chris's behalf.

Ian and I have different recollections about what happened next. Ian claims that Doctor Piaget used the words "possible schizophrenia." For the life of me, I do not remember him saying that. What I remember him saying was this: "Chris needs help. He needs medication."

"Medication for what?" I asked.

"Of course," Doctor Piaget continued, "I could be mistaken, and I cannot diagnose ('possible schizophrenia,' claimed Ian), as I am not a psychiatrist, but in my view, because he's decompensating, the sooner he gets on medication the better. I've heard that North America is way ahead of Switzerland when it comes to these things."

Doctor Piaget suggested that one of us accompany Chris back to the University of Toronto and make sure that he got into the student residence. He thought that being in familiar surroundings where people knew him, rather than living off campus, as we told him Chris was planning to do, would be less stressful for Chris.

"And before you leave," Doctor Piaget advised, "ask the head of Chris's college—without divulging any details—for a referral to a psychiatrist. Give the psychiatrist my contact details and ask him to call me before I go on vacation. I'm leaving in ten days."

Ian and I left the office, horribly shaken. The gravity of the situation made me want to stick my head further into the sand. This couldn't be happening to Chris and to our family.

Over the next few days I spent a lot of time online, plugging in search terms like "depression" and "psychiatric diagnoses," but I didn't know what I was looking for and none of the diagnoses I read about seemed to apply. The psychiatric terminology was new to me.

Oppositional defiant disorder. That could be any willful child, but it certainly wasn't Chris. *Borderline personality disorder.* Definitely a pass. The descriptions of schizophrenia didn't seem to fit, either. I wasn't aware of my son having visual or auditory hallucinations or disorganized thoughts. His complex, metaphorical way of expressing himself didn't strike me as disorganized.

I focused on Doctor Piaget's disclaimer: "Of course, I could be mistaken." I concluded that Chris was not mentally ill, that he was just going through some very peculiar phase, and that Doctor Piaget was indeed mistaken about Chris's state of mind.

"He said he wasn't certain," I said to Ian. "He's not a psychiatrist; he doesn't really know. He could be wrong." I held out that hope.

Despite my reservations, Ian and I moved heaven and earth and made lots of phone calls to get Chris back into a residence hall for the coming term. His flight to Toronto was just days away.

Once the housing arrangements were settled, I got myself a seat on Chris's flight. Next, I phoned the dean of students at Trinity College for a referral to a psychiatrist, as Doctor Piaget had instructed. The dean recommended David Jones at the university's student health clinic.

I phoned the clinic and made an appointment for Chris and me to meet Doctor Jones on the following Monday, before classes began. *This will be relatively straightforward,* I thought. *I'll explain what's going on, and he'll assure me that nothing is wrong—or at least nothing that Chris won't grow out of.*

The worst outcome I expected was that Chris would be given a pill—an antidepressant, maybe, if Doctor Jones believed that depression was the problem—and life would return to normal.

I sent Doctor Jones an e-mail, urging him to contact Doctor Piaget before he went on vacation. I included Doctor Piaget's contact details and the dates he would be out of the office.

Ian volunteered to phone Doctor Jones before the appointment to explain our concerns. I declined his offer, for several reasons. I wanted Doctor Jones to evaluate Chris's current condition for himself; I was confident about my ability to describe Chris's mental state when we met in person; and I thought Doctor Jones would be conferring with Doctor Piaget. Ian's intervention on top of that seemed like too much additional pressure in an already tense situation. I was frightened, and I was attempting to avoid what turned out to be a painful truth. This was pure denial on my part.

Louise Hay, author of *You Can Heal Your Life* and other inspirational books, says that all human diseases can be attributed to one of two mental patterns: fear or anger. It was becoming increasingly clear to me that my avoidance was rooted in fear. My mental pattern would have to change if Chris and I were going to successfully navigate our journey.

Chapter 6

✳ Talking to God

CHRIS WAS LATE for our Monday morning appointment at
the Health Services clinic. I waited outside the building for him for
twenty minutes; by the time we got inside, our scheduled time was
almost half over.

My heart was pounding as I cleared my throat and told Doctor
Jones my concerns, which centered on Chris's poor grades and changed
personality. My son was becoming untidy and was often late, I said,
and he had unrealistic ideas about his own abilities. I talked about the
driving lesson that got cut short. I described the Ophelia drama but
omitted mention of the turd incident, wanting to spare Chris further
humiliation and assuming (incorrectly, as it turned out) that Doctor
Jones had probably already learned about it from Doctor Piaget.

As I chattered on, I realized that I must have seemed like an over-
bearing and overanxious mother. Surely Doctor Jones had heard all this
before: A talented kid flounders during his first year at university, to
the disbelief of his doting parents. After hearing me out, Doctor Jones
turned to Chris and asked him why he was causing me such concern.

Chris's face lit up as he launched a charm offensive, smiling his
old self-deprecating smile.

He's got good teeth, I found myself thinking. *Never needed braces, never had a cavity.*

The way Chris told it, he'd been too busy having fun the previous year to bother with his studies.

"I have been distracted by parties, student debates and co-ed rugby matches," he said grandly. "This year, I am determined to do well."

Doctor Jones bought Chris's explanation. Having only just met Chris, he might not have noticed Chris's stilted speech, which, to me, seemed both odd and falsely erudite.

At that point, I knew I had failed to clue Doctor Jones in to the gravity of the situation. Ian would have bluntly told him: "My son is mentally ill. Doctor Piaget thinks he should be on medication." I did not state outright that Chris's family feared that he was mentally ill. As his mother, I didn't want to rat on him to a doctor. To me, declaring that my own son was crazy seemed ... *disloyal,* like I didn't love or appreciate him and was now turning him over to the authorities to see what they could do with him.

Having only Chris's bravura performance to go by, how could Doctor Jones see what I was seeing? His face gave no hint of concern that Chris was experiencing anything more than a short-term condition that would resolve itself as Chris adapted to college life.

I urged him to start seeing Chris on a weekly basis. He asked Chris if that was okay.

Chris didn't like the idea. "Maybe I could see you again in January," he said.

"No, Chris," I pressed. "October is more like it."

We left the office with an appointment for Chris to return in a month. I was acutely aware that I had fumbled the ball. My fears had stood in the way of getting Chris the help he needed. I had not shared enough critical information. The consequences of my being me were becoming apparent.

Several months later, I learned that although Doctor Jones had extensive experience as a therapist and as a teacher, he was a psychologist—not a psychiatrist. Like Doctor Piaget, he could not prescribe medication. Furthermore, he had not contacted Doctor Piaget as I had requested, which meant that when Chris and I showed up that day, Doctor Jones had no information about Chris's history or the nature of our visit, other than the picture I painted. Ian's impulse to speak to Doctor Jones ahead of time was entirely justified.

We heard little from Chris after I kissed him goodbye outside the entrance to the clinic. He rarely called us, nor did he write to us the way he used to. We arranged regular conference calls to make sure he was on track with his schoolwork, and on one occasion asked if he had seen Doctor Jones. He had seen him once, he said.

"You know, it's nice to talk with Doctor Jones, and I think he enjoys talking to me, but I don't think he really needs to see me."

As had happened when he'd met with Doctor Piaget, Chris seemed to think that he and Doctor Jones were on the same level professionally. This grandiosity was similar to the overconfidence that I had observed with Chris's aborted driving lesson and his choice to skip first-year math.

Chris wasn't writing to his parents during this period, but he was sending cheerful, upbeat letters to his brothers. His issues seemed to be with Ian and me, and we took this as a sign that he was trying to become independent. Our flagging hope was that this phase would pass without any dramatic interventions on our part, and Chris would learn to cope with the stresses of college life.

My birthday in early November passed with no word from Chris. He left a message a day later on my answering machine at work. He must have wanted to avoid talking to me, so he called at 11:00 p.m. Toronto time, 5:00 a.m. our time. His voice sounded hollow and cold and vague.

"So happy birthday, I guess."

Click.

I called him a couple of days later.

"Chris, hi. What's up?"

"Oh, not much. Talking to God and all." He laughed nervously, as if to dismiss his offhanded remark.

I reminded him that a plane reservation had been made for his return to Geneva on December 13. "The date can be changed," I told him, "but you'll have to act quickly."

Ian and I had been pestering Chris to let us know when his final exams would be over but we hadn't heard from him, so Ian had gone ahead and made a reservation after learning that most first-year exams were over in early December. We wanted to allow Chris a comfortable margin of time in case he had a late exam or wanted to hang around Toronto for a few days.

"Really, Chris," I said, exasperated, "we resent having to do what someone your age should be able to do for himself."

Chris didn't immediately respond to my lecture. He breathed into the phone for what seemed like an eternity before apologizing.

"I'm sorry," he said. "It was silly of me to be so negligent."

I exploded. "I'm not looking for an apology, Chris! What I want is for you to take charge of YOUR responsibilities!"

I wasn't the only one to notice Chris's lack of follow-through. My sister Jane lived in Toronto. During one of our phone conversations, she mentioned that she'd been trying to reach Chris for weeks to invite him over for dinner and had left many messages on his answering machine. He eventually called her one night after eleven o'clock. He told her he'd been getting together daily with a Singaporean friend to pray.

I knew that Chris was attending chapel services at the college, but learning about the additional daily prayer time was unsettling. To me, excessive religiosity is a sign of mental instability.

My concerns were soon borne out. A crisis was about to erupt.

Chapter 7

✸ *Diagnosis*

ON WEDNESDAY EVENING, December 10, 2003, I was at home when the telephone rang. The Trinity College chaplain, Peter Strand, introduced himself. He knew Chris from his volunteer position as an acolyte in the college chapel and had met Ian on a couple of occasions the previous year.

"I am sorry to have to tell you this," Reverend Strand said, "but Chris has been behaving very strangely. He needs a psychiatric evaluation."

My mouth went dry and my legs threatened to give out from under me. I could barely focus on what the voice at the other end of the line was saying. My heart was pounding hard, as if I had just climbed several flights of stairs.

I walked, phone in hand, to Taylor's room and lay down on the bed while I continued to listen.

"I know this is difficult for you," the chaplain said, "but, if you'd like, I can make an appointment for Chris at the student health clinic."

With a heavy heart, I gave my consent. I told the chaplain that my sister would be a good local contact and that I would let her know what was happening. We agreed to keep in touch by e-mail and by phone.

I immediately called Ian in Kuwait, where he'd been working for a few days. He reacted calmly to the news and promised me he'd be home soon. "We'll sort this all out then."

In retrospect, the chaplain's words seemed almost comical; he wasn't telling us anything we didn't already know. Getting Chris evaluated had been the point of the visit with Doctor Jones, back in September, at the same student health clinic!

Late in the day on Thursday, I received an e-mail from Reverend Strand. He had met Chris at 9:00 a.m., Toronto time, and together they had walked to the Health Services building. Chris signed in, but after waiting for twenty minutes, he stood up and calmly walked out of the waiting room without uttering a word.

As Chris had left his coat on a hook, the chaplain assumed he had gone to the restroom down the hall. When he didn't return after five minutes, Reverend Strand went looking for him. He searched for half an hour before giving up and returning to the clinic. There, he spoke with the psychologist (Doctor Jones, for all I know!), who suggested that, although Chris was probably not a danger to himself or others, he should nevertheless be admitted for observation to the local psychiatric hospital. The Centre for Addiction and Mental Health (CAMH), a provincial inpatient facility, was about a twenty-minute walk from Trinity College.

Reverend Strand was confident that Chris would come back in due course; he would make sure that Chris was taken to CAMH, he wrote. In the meantime, he suggested I ask my sister to contact him so he could apprise her of any new developments. He assured me that Chris was not aggressive in any way; he was known to be an intelligent and gentle young man by students and staff at Trinity. They would want to do all they could to encourage and support him.

About an hour later, I received another e-mail from Reverend Strand letting me know that the college authorities and the campus police had been alerted to keep an eye out for Chris.

* * *

I called Jane Friday afternoon (Geneva time) and told her the grave news that Chris was seriously ill.

"He needs to be evaluated by a psychiatrist," I said. "The Trinity chaplain will see that he gets to CAMH—as soon as he turns up."

Jane told me she'd phoned Chris several times after inviting him to her house for an early Christmas dinner, but he refused to commit to a specific date.

"I was frustrated by his behavior, but I didn't think that much about it," Jane said. "I figured he was busy with exams and had a lot on his plate."

Now, his attempts to avoid her made sense.

I asked Jane to contact Peter Strand to discuss strategies for getting Chris to the hospital.

"Yes, of course. I'll phone him right away," she said. "I'm supposed to see Chris tomorrow morning to give him Christmas presents to take to Geneva. I do hope he's okay."

A few hours later, I opened my inbox and found a message from the dean. Chris had returned to the college, coatless, shortly after 8:00 p.m. on Friday evening, nose dripping from the cold. When the dean spoke with him twenty minutes later, his answers were clear and brief. He was sorry everyone had been worried, but "there was no point" in seeing the doctor, so he'd left. He didn't say where he'd been, and he promptly left again, telling the dean he was off to visit one of his friends in the residence hall and would be back later that evening.

The dean said the staff at the college was trying to keep a general lookout for Chris without being too intrusive. He thought that a good sleep might be better for Chris that night than a long wait at the hospital.

Late Saturday afternoon, I received a brief e-mail from Reverend Strand telling me that Chris had been admitted to CAMH and was doing well. He planned to visit him on Sunday and would contact me with a further progress report. At least now I knew where Chris was and that he would get the help he needed.

As I got up from the computer to begin dinner preparations, Jane called, weeping copious tears. She and Jessica, the dean's assistant, had taken Chris to the hospital earlier that day. They sat in the waiting room while he was interviewed by a psychiatrist.

"They told me it's schizz . . . schizz . . . *schizophrenia!*" She could hardly say the word. "Twenty-five percent chance it's bipolar disorder, but they don't think it is. It was awful. Chris looked so lost. They kept asking me if he uses drugs. I told them I didn't think so, and Chris said he doesn't."

Schizophrenia! At last, an explanation for Chris's strange behavior: He was suffering from schizophrenia. My heart leapt into my throat.

Jane and I agreed to stay in close contact over the next few days. I felt terrible that I hadn't confided in her sooner; learning the extent and duration of Chris's problems came like a bolt out of the blue for her, and she was understandably shaken. I had wanted to protect Chris's dignity and privacy and, foolishly, I'd hoped he was going through a phase that would pass.

I wandered around the apartment in a daze. I still had to break the news to Chris's brothers. I asked them to turn off the video game they were playing in the living room.

"We're almost finished, Mom," the pair said in unison, their eyes glued to the screen.

"Now," I insisted. "We need to talk about your brother."

Dutifully, Alex paused the game. He and Taylor gave me their full attention. I explained that Chris was in the hospital and had been diagnosed with schizophrenia. I did my best to remain calm, composed, and in command of the situation, but my sad face and flat tone reflected the inner turmoil I was feeling.

I quickly realized that I knew very little about this thing called schizophrenia, so I couldn't fully explain what was wrong with Chris. I could only give his condition a name. Well, at least I finally had that.

Fourteen-year-old Taylor piped up. "Mom, I did a project last year on schizophrenia and the drugs are really good. He'll be okay."

I wasn't as sure as Taylor that Chris would be okay, but I applauded his spirit.

Chapter 8

❋ My Name is Legion

ON SUNDAY EVENING, I got an e-mail from the dean summarizing a conversation he'd had with Jessica, his assistant. Jessica had visited with Chris for close to twenty minutes earlier that day and, to Chris's delight, had brought him his guitar.

Chris was about to be moved to the Early Psychosis unit of the hospital, Jessica reported, and he seemed to be more aware of his surroundings than he'd been during the fall term. He was now making eye contact, and his speech was clearer. They joked about the food at the hospital, comparing it to the food service at Trinity.

Chris told Jessica that he wanted his family to know he was eating okay, doing fine, feeling healthy, and looking forward to coming home soon. The doctors thought he might be released as an outpatient the following week, so he didn't want his plane ticket canceled.

The dean thought the news sounded encouraging. During the fall semester, he wrote, he'd sometimes found Chris sitting alone in the residence hall—on a bench in the main floor hallway or in the darkened computer room—staring into space. In the dining hall, too, Chris often sat by himself, seemingly content to be alone.

The dean had learned from my son's friends that Chris sometimes followed them to a pub but declined to go inside.

Reverend Strand later told me that Chris sometimes stood for long periods in the college courtyard, like a statue. Once, he stood in the rain for hours, thoroughly soaking his new tweed jacket.

Jane told me—much later—that when she and Jessica went to clean out Chris's room, it was littered with plastic bags of excrement and bottles of urine. Jane noticed that Chris kept a copy on his bookshelf of Karl Menninger's classic book, *Whatever Became of Sin?*

I wondered what the feces and urine meant and why my son was so preoccupied with notions of good and evil. Months later, when I probed into the reasons for his lack of eye contact, Chris said he couldn't make eye contact with people because his eyes could harm them and their eyes could harm him. This belief explained, in part, his reading choices and why he spent every day of that term on his knees in prayer.

For a few confusing days following Chris's admission, I didn't know who to contact at CAMH to find out what was going on—and no one from the treatment team contacted me. I had to rely upon the dean, the chaplain, and my sister for reports about my son's condition.

Three days passed before I got through to one of the doctors familiar with Chris's case. I quickly realized that Jessica's optimism about the speed of Chris's recovery was unfounded. Chris's belief that he was going to be allowed to come home turned out to be wishful thinking on his part.

"Well, he's not one of our sickest patients," the doctor said. Apparently, he was not one of their better patients either. Her tone implied that Chris was sick, very sick.

"Our team doesn't think it's a good idea for Chris to leave the hospital," she told me. "He's a voluntary patient, but if he pushes to leave the hospital to get on a plane," she warned, "we'll change his status to certifiable." After a pause, she added, "This is not our preferred option. We'd rather keep the goodwill and trust. As a voluntary patient Chris will be given a day pass and allowed to go back to his room at Trinity to gather a few things."

I promised the doctor that our family would visit Chris as soon as we could arrange the plane tickets. Ian was back from Kuwait, and we had decided that we would spend Christmas in Toronto. Peter Strand had kindly offered us the use of his house over the holidays while he and his family were visiting relatives in the United States. We were overwhelmed by his generosity.

The plane reservations took about a week to arrange, and during that time I learned firsthand about the prolonged effect of anxiety on the nervous system. The faces of people I passed on crowded sidewalks grew sinister. Images oozed off commercial billboards like a Salvador Dali painting, the bright colors bleeding into each other. My adrenaline was surging; my heart was continuously pounding.

I'd never taken anti-anxiety medication before, but I felt I needed it now. My doctor gave me a prescription for Xanax, a benzodiazepine, which helped me to function at work and to sleep at night.

The night before leaving for Toronto, I dug out my King James Bible for the first time in years. I randomly opened it to the Gospel of Mark (Chapter 5), where Jesus encounters a man possessed by demons. Jesus asks the man's name and he answers, "My name is Legion: for we are many." Jesus cures him, performing a miracle.

I was struck by the realization that mental illness has been for around a long time, elated at the idea that miracles can happen—until another thought dampened my fledgling hope. *If Jesus cured the demon-possessed, why today are there so many men and women living on the edge of society, in our streets and homeless shelters? What has happened to our collective belief system that we now see mental illness as a chronic condition? Why do so many of us Christians who speak of faith and miracles often behave as if prophets lived centuries ago, not now, and miraculous cures ONLY happened in the Bible?*

I'd never been a devout Christian, although I'd attended church regularly for most of my life. Going to church on Sundays instilled in me a moral code that had been followed by my parents and their parents before them, and which I, in turn, passed on to my children. The ritual of attending church meant very little to me from a spiritual point of view, however. I couldn't wait for the service to finish so I could get back to "real" life. The idea of prophets and miracles struck me as preposterous, but, nonetheless, it was a convention I had to go along with if I claimed to be a believer.

I closed the book and turned off the light, wondering if perhaps I'd been too dismissive in the past of the Bible's many miracles. There had to be some useful messages in these stories that could speak to me, even today.

Before drifting off to sleep, I reviewed what I knew about Jesus: He was the son of God; he was a healer and a teacher. He was the light.

The healing power of *light* would reveal itself to me in due course.

Chapter 9

❋ The Centre for Addiction and Mental Health

I ARRIVED IN TORONTO on December 22, a day ahead of the rest of the family. John, an old friend and husband to Maret, my graduate school roommate, met me at Pearson International Airport late that afternoon and drove me straight to CAMH to see Chris.

Appearances can be deceiving, I told myself as John and I walked from the parking lot to the entrance of the drab concrete fortress. I was eager to see Chris, but worried about what condition I might find him in.

The interior of the building was just as depressing as the exterior. There was no reception desk, no hustle and bustle of visitors and staff crisscrossing the lobby like in a regular hospital. John and I took the elevator up to the Early Psychosis unit. I introduced myself to the nurse, who was barricaded behind a glass window. She got up from her chair to unlock the door for us and then called to another nurse, who disappeared briefly. When she returned, Chris was with her.

His face lit up when he saw me. "Hi Mom," he said quietly.

I gave him a big hug and introduced John, who excused himself and went to sit in the lounge while Chris and I walked down the hall to his room.

A surprisingly well-groomed young man shuffled stiffly by, staring straight ahead, his arms seemingly bolted to his side. I realized that my son was also shuffling along the corridor, head not turning, with the same zombie-like appearance and gait.

Chris's room was simple: a single bed, a gray blanket, cracked rubber tile flooring. His clothes were in a plastic bag on the floor; the rest of his meager possessions were strewn around the room. I immediately set about tidying up. I tossed a few socks into the bag and straightened up the bed.

"Where's the belt for your bathrobe?" I asked, regretting the words as soon as they left my mouth.

"I had to hand over anything I might hang myself with," he said, grinning slightly. "I'll get it back when I leave."

Through the locked window, I got a stunning and surreal view of the CN Tower, at that time the world's tallest freestanding structure. Built to serve the communication needs of the region, the tower contains microwave receptors and is topped by a 335-foot antenna. The observation deck, 1,136 feet above the ground, is a popular tourist destination.

This is the view they give patients in the psychosis unit? I thought, picturing paranoid patients ranting about government spies and coded messages. *Somebody sure has a wicked sense of humor!*

After Ian arrived in Toronto, we met with one of Chris's doctors and the social worker in charge of his care. At the end of our meeting, we were handed a guide to first-episode psychosis. I wanted to throw it in the trash. The dramatic black-and-yellow image on the cover featured hands pushing down on a head. It was at once clinical, ominous, depressing, discouraging, and fatalistic.

The pamphlet described different kinds of psychoses. Was the patient more disorganized, more depressed, or more paranoid? A psychotic individual presenting with symptoms from all three categories would be classified as "undifferentiated." Undifferentiated psychosis appeared to have the least hopeful prognosis.

When I read the clinical descriptions of psychosis, I became depressed and anxious. The pamphlet stated clearly that a better outcome could be achieved if the person was treated early. I was afraid we'd caught Chris's schizophrenia too late, that he was not in early psychosis, and therefore not "fixable."

I counted back on the fingers of my hands the months that had passed since Chris started having symptoms. According to my count, he was borderline "early." I felt extremely guilty about letting his illness go untreated for so long and for ignoring—or refusing to see—the danger signs.

Because of the holidays, the doctors made a special exception and allowed Chris to stay with us for a few days. We left the hospital dispensary armed with Risperdal (risperidone) and a sealed envelope containing two pills that Chris was supposed to take "if needed"—whatever that meant.

John and Maret had invited our family for Christmas Eve dinner at their home in Thornhill, an upscale suburban area just north of the city limits. Spending the evening with them and their three children gave us a wonderful distraction. Chris sat quietly by himself on the couch, sipping a diet soda and occasionally smiling like a kindly old grandfather, observing, but not participating in, the festivity going on around him.

During the long drive back to the Strands' house, however, Chris became exceedingly agitated. He badly needed to urinate. I looked at my watch. Midnight. We spied an all-night donut shop. Ian circled the block looking for parking while Chris and I headed toward the shop. The temperature was well below freezing, and my toes were numb. Chris started hopping up and down and walking round and round in circles. Using all my wiles, I coaxed him inside. I asked the girl behind the counter for the key to the washroom and rushed it over to Chris. He took one look at the female shape on the fob and refused to take the key.

"That's for the women's washroom," he said.

"For crying out loud, Chris! There is only one washroom here. Just go pee!"

My appeal to reason went unheeded. Chris was not thinking rationally, so reasonable arguments didn't register in his disordered mind. Then, suddenly, he bolted out of the store.

Frightened, I ran after him. I didn't know where he had gone, and Ian was nowhere in sight. I paced the sidewalk in front of the shop, stamping my boots to keep my circulation going and feeling quite helpless.

When Chris reappeared, he kept a wary distance of several feet. Ian showed up soon afterwards, and between the two of us we convinced Chris to get into the car. When we arrived at the Strands' house, his pants were soaking wet. He showered and went to bed.

I remembered the pills that we were supposed to give him "if needed"; they'd been in my purse the entire time. "If needed" now meant to me: "You'll know it when you see it." I prayed I'd never see "it" again.

And what would those pills have done to him? I wondered. *Knocked him out cold?*

I was clearly an amateur in these matters. By the time Christmas Eve's wild ride was over, I was more than ready to take Chris back to the hospital and let the professionals handle him.

The next morning, Christmas Day, we opened the presents we'd brought from Geneva. Socks, CDs, and shirts for all.

Maret had taken Chris shopping earlier in the week, so he had presents to share with us, too. He gave Ian, Alex, and Taylor hanging brass ornaments from Chinatown, and he gave me two cut-glass paperweights. (The smaller one was engraved with the words "souvenir of Hong Kong 1999.") I recalled that in *A Beautiful Mind*, John Nash presented Alicia (his future wife) with a similar gift, chosen because of the colorful refractions that could be seen in the glass. *Just a coincidence,* I wondered, *or is there a message here?*

During our stay at the Strands' house, our family got acquainted with the neighborhood. We located an Internet café where we could all read our e-mails and the boys could play video games. Our parish priest in Geneva wrote that he'd been praying for Chris and our family. He urged us to lean into our faith by inviting Christ Jesus into our son's healing.

At the café, Chris kept his winter jacket, hat, and gloves on while he worked the video game keyboard. He reminded me of Glenn Gould, the classical pianist. A native Torontonian, Glenn Gould, among his many other eccentricities, was famous for wearing a woolen coat and hat while performing, even in the hottest weather.

When Chris was young, his piano teachers said he was naturally musical, and he was especially strong in sight-reading, but he didn't apply himself and eventually stopped playing. One of the few times I ever saw him truly excited was when we bought him his first guitar, soon after our move to Geneva. His face flushed, his "thank you" fluctuated over several octaves, and he dashed to his room to get acquainted with his new instrument.

The Strands had a guitar, and it quickly became the focus of Chris's attention. I watched as, again and again, Chris picked up the guitar and played a few riffs before putting it down and walking away. Then, he would hesitate, turn around, and come back to play a few more riffs. The playing seemed to calm him, and the guitar spoke for him during this time, when he was almost mute.

One night, we took the subway to a theater downtown to see the third installment in *The Lord of the Rings* trilogy, *The Return of the King*. Chris was enchanted by the fantasy and, perhaps, overstimulated. During the train ride back, he talked excitedly about the film in a crazy, word-salad rush of emotive gobbledygook. The sound of his voice carried in the almost-vacant subway car like wind in a tunnel: "While in those subwaywagginsbaggins carry palaces to the Strand, where hobbits mire and scream to the Gloin, yet the rings brings not."

Darkish speech of hobbits miring very, very frightening for this mother who prided herself on being well-grounded and practical. I hoped that a stay at CAMH would bring an end to all this nonsense. I simply did not possess the skills to handle this level of drama.

After Chris returned to the hospital, Ian and I met several times with Doctor Luke Vandemaele and Tracy, the social worker. Both were nice, earnest people in their early to mid-thirties.

"How long will Chris have to be on the medications?" Ian asked.

Doctor Vandemaele, no doubt aware that we might be disappointed by his answer, paused before replying. "If he's like most people with schizophrenia, he'll probably need medications for the rest of his life. Management of this illness requires trial and error to find the most effective medication, or combination of medications."

Seeing our crestfallen faces, he quickly added, "Today's medications are much better than the old ones, and they have fewer side effects."

Tracy, perhaps in an effort to provide us with some reason for hope, referred to anticipated medical breakthroughs, as research was underway to better understand and treat mental illness. "In the next five to ten years, there will be better drugs and perhaps a clearer understanding of the role of genetics in the onset of mental illness," she said. "There is no cure for schizophrenia, but the medications these days are extremely good."

Looking around at the drab surroundings, I found it hard to share Tracy's optimism. Even five years struck me as too long a time for someone in young adulthood to put his life on hold.

Several days later, Ian and I went over our family history with Doctor Vandemaele and his immediate superior. As had happened with the psychologist in Geneva, clinical depression, anorexia nervosa, and mild obsessive-compulsive disorder didn't even get a nod. These clinicians weren't interested in my ten-month pregnancy and the lack of movement in utero, and they had no answers for us when we asked what might have caused Chris's schizophrenia.

Ian and I insisted that the doctors order an MRI (magnetic resonance imaging) scan to make sure that Chris didn't have a brain tumor. Given the stabbing pain in his forehead, and the head-tapping that followed, we thought that tests were warranted to rule out possible medical causes for his symptoms.

The MRI revealed that nothing was abnormal about Chris's brain (a huge relief). Where, then, was the problem? The diagnosis of schizophrenia seemed to be based on observations of behavior and doctors' judgments, not on scientific evidence (hard data). The diagnostic process struck us as being more of an art than a science.

Both Doctor Vandemaele and Tracy talked a lot about "recovery," without specifying what that meant. We asked what Chris would be like when he recovered.

"Was he well-adjusted before his behavior deteriorated? Did he have friends? Did he do well in school?" the doctor asked.

We answered yes to all questions. Prior social and academic successes, apparently, were good signs.

Almost as an afterthought, Doctor Vandemaele posed an unusual question: "What was Chris like around the age of ten?"

Ian and I had to think a bit on this one. All we remembered was that Chris had been overweight, and he was into playing a fantasy card game with one of his friends. It never occurred to me to ask Doctor Vandemaele what was so special about age ten, but his question seemed to suggest that schizophrenia could be predicted years before it actually manifested.

In early January, I flew home to Geneva; Ian, Taylor, and Alex followed two days later. During my last visit to the hospital, the doctors had advised Ian and me not to read too much about schizophrenia. Considering how hopeless and depressed I'd felt after reading the hospital's pamphlet, and accepting the medical model and treatment plan as it had been explained to us, I saw no reason to investigate further.

I know now that the medical model is only one approach to health and wellness, and it's an approach that some people reject in favor of more holistic alternatives. Had I known then that other treatments were available outside of hospitals and psychiatrists' offices, I would gladly have explored them from the outset.

Without a map to guide us, we simply followed the directions given to us by those who claimed to know the territory.

Chapter 10

Things Fall Apart ✳

MARET E-MAILED ME shortly after I arrived home. Toronto was experiencing record low temperatures, and she had braved the elements to bring Chris a bottled fruit drink and a small cake in belated honor of his birthday.

"He seems coherent and is eager to plan his next semester of courses," she wrote. She offered to meet with the head of Student Accessibility Services to discuss a plan for Chris to resume his courses. I welcomed her kind offer.

Ian and I were booked for a ten-day vacation in Thailand in mid-January. We thought about canceling but decided we desperately needed the rest. We trusted that Chris was being taken care of in the hospital, and we knew he was visited weekly by Maret, Jane, and Reverend Strand.

I asked my family doctor in Geneva for a different medication than Xanax, which is intended for short-term use only. He recommended Paxil, saying that in a week to ten days I'd be seeing "blue skies all the way." A few days later, poolside in Phuket, the skies *were* blue—all the way! I felt totally carefree.

For three mornings in a row, as I lay in bed in the hotel room I experienced a strange sensation. My legs shook and jumped for several seconds, as if jolted by a strong electrical current. I figured I was still adjusting to the Paxil. I wasn't frightened, but perhaps I should have been. It's possible that I was experiencing a withdrawal effect from the Xanax, a benzodiazepine. (Benzos are highly addictive.) This troubling symptom should have made me question why I was taking drugs at all.

Ian and I checked e-mail frequently for news about Chris. Maret wrote that she was working on his course registration with Student Accessibility Services, and she volunteered to help him get organized. Incredibly, the doctors at CAMH thought Chris would be able to attend his math and environmental science classes while he was an inpatient. Equally incredibly, given all that came later, we thought so too.

With Chris's immediate future looking brighter, my husband and I enjoyed the rest of our vacation. Boarding the plane in Bangkok at the end of our stay, we felt totally relaxed.

During the flight, I noticed Ian chortling over the movie he was watching and I decided to watch it too. *Tais-toi! (Shut Up!)* stars Jean Reno as a convict who, unwittingly, becomes shackled to Gérard Depardieu, a sort of village idiot from the French town of Montargy. In one hilarious scene, the two men escape from a psychiatric hospital while wearing straitjackets. Ian and I were practically rolling in the aisles with laughter, tears streaming down our faces. Never had mental illness been so much fun! The Paxil had definitely kicked in.

Soon after our holiday in Thailand, Chris's promising situation began to change. In late January 2004, we received a lengthy e-mail from Doctor Vandemaele, who wrote that although Chris had initially responded well to treatment, his condition had worsened. Believing that the world was going to end, he'd stopped eating and drinking and resigned himself to his fate. He failed to comprehend that his illness could be treated. Fearing that Chris was in danger of harming himself, the hospital staff had changed his status to "involuntary" and deemed him incapable of making treatment decisions. Chris had filed an appeal.

Ten days earlier, Doctor Vandemaele informed us, Chris had become disoriented while out on a pass and returned to the hospital an hour late. Although no physical harm had befallen him, with the temperature outside hovering around -30°C (-22°F), he was told that he wouldn't be allowed out again unless he was accompanied by a nurse. Considering his need for supervision, the university asked him to withdraw from his courses. He rapidly descended into a deep depression. If he didn't improve, Doctor Vandemaele warned, electroshock therapy might be necessary.

Because Chris had appealed the hospital's finding of incapacity, no new treatment could be ordered until a hearing was held. Doctor Vandemaele asked that either Ian or I be designated as the decision-maker for treatment decisions. He said Chris had a right to appeal our decisions as well.

At least Chris was showing some initiative, I thought. I discussed the situation with Ian, who agreed to be the primary decision-maker. Though the worsening of Chris's condition distressed us, we fully appreciated the need for him to remain at CAMH, even if he wasn't there voluntarily. We couldn't risk letting him freeze to death on the streets.

Given Chris's preoccupation with religious and existential themes, Doctor Vandemaele suggested that Chris might benefit from speaking with Reverend Strand. As Christians, Ian and I believed that God cared about Chris as an individual, was aware of his situation, and was working through the members of the team at CAMH and in other ways to heal him.

We phoned Chris to try to get across some simple points, such as the importance of eating regularly. We told him he would eventually get better if he took his medicine and accepted treatment. We all loved him, we said, and were counting on him to be a part of our future, even if he was sick and required treatment. We urged him to be open to visits from Reverend Strand, who went to see Chris soon after we informed him of this latest crisis.

The chaplain sat quietly with Chris and held his hand in prayer. Subsequently, Chris dropped his challenge to the hospital's determination of incapacity to make decisions. He resumed eating and drinking, thus avoiding the very real possibility of electroshock therapy. He was then put on an initial 37.5 mg dose of the antidepressant Effexor (venlafaxine) in addition to the 6 mg per day of risperidone he had been taking. Ian and I were grateful that this latest crisis had come to an end.

Doctor Vandemaele concluded that Chris had schizophrenia with a secondary depression. Finding the two together was not uncommon in the first presentation of the illness, the doctor said in an e-mail. He assured us that effective treatments for both conditions were available, and he expected that Chris would continue to improve after he started taking the antidepressant. If all went well, Chris would be ready to come home in early March.

I had to agree that Chris met the criteria for a diagnosis of schizophrenia, but I thought his depression could be situational, prompted by being forced to drop out of university while residing in a mental hospital.

Chris later wrote about his experience at CAMH, and he agreed to let me include his reflections here.

> After the admittance process and signing forms, then "being patient" for two nights while my file was scrutinized, I found the staff to be expert, punctual, and clean, though "caring" was at first a stretch. As my stay grew longer, I got to know one or two nurses who I could talk with and who would take me for a coffee, a big thrill, believe me. I found myself and all the other patients (a flexible roster with some turnover) to be unique from each other. Unlike at college, I was looking for special qualities in other patients. There were a variety of ages (18 to 25) and professions (students, day workers), and life stories (some were Torontonians, some had moved from abroad). I tended to talk with

the philosophical patients, but it was the real rebels that broke the routine of the day, from not putting out cigarettes to a surprising mix of violent and passive resistance. I got to see it from all angles, from helpless patient to prisoner to getting along with patients who shared food and time with me as they would their best friend. The doctors were a little scary at first, using a mix of intimidation and piercing logic to keep me compliant. I may have felt this way about them because I was offered a form to legally contest my clinical order to stay, and was not initially in a mood to make the best of things. Really, though, my first doctor was dead-on when she insisted I stay. The truth did indeed hurt, but we sort of compromised when she left and I agreed not to quit the hospital. My treatment was primarily with medication, but I did speak to a psychiatrist once a week, which was helpful; a rational mind made me feel that there was logic if not reason to my stay. Mostly though, I kept my emotions to myself. However, my emotional stability was pretty shot to begin with. I got help from a lovely nurse, a veteran whose experience I trusted. It was nice to hear telephone calls, but we were largely left to ourselves. The mood was lightened with Karaoke night especially.[1]

My son had been much more aware of what was happening to him and around him, it seems, than anyone who had observed him in the hospital could have imagined.

Chapter 11

✳ A Glimpse of HOPE

IN EARLY MARCH, Maret and her ten-year-old daughter, Jenna, packed up Chris's room at the college. Two suitcases would be brought back to Geneva; boxes of books and bedding would be delivered to the basements of both sets of Chris's grandparents in Ontario. After the work was done, Maret and Jenna popped in to see Chris at the hospital and they all went for a walk.

Maret sent me an e-mail, telling of Chris's courage and kindness while working hard to "keep it all together" and how he opened doors for Jenna and smiled at her chatter. "He's still not talking a lot, but you can definitely communicate through smiles, nods, shakes of the head."

Soon after, Ian and I got the go-ahead from CAMH to bring Chris home. We flew to Toronto and again met with Doctor Vandemaele and Tracy.

Chris was heavily drugged. I couldn't imagine how we were going to get him on a plane the next day, but we trusted that everything would work out okay.

That evening, the three of us took a taxi to the Air Canada Centre to see the Toronto Maple Leafs play the Florida Panthers. (At one hundred and fifty bucks a pop, I was appalled by the ticket price. I was as innocent then about the state of professional hockey as I was about the profession of psychiatry.)

We threaded our way through lines of stretch limos, passing men in tailored suits and dark glasses, visual reminders that money was the real game. I could have sworn I saw an eight-year-old boy tugging an agent's sleeve, imploring, "Say it ain't so, Joe."

The game was broadcast on a giant screen that was impossible to ignore, despite the fact that the action was on the ice. Forced to listen to stupid jingles and to watch dancing mascots, I felt my IQ slipping.

Every few minutes, a player rammed an opponent into the boards, a cue for other players to angrily swarm up and continue the clobbering— just enough clobbering for spectators to feel they'd gotten their money's worth before the referee blew his whistle, the game stopped, and the player was sent to the penalty box. This start-and-stop process made the game v-e-r-r-y slow (on top of being v-e-r-r-y boring).

To my left was an inebriated fellow from my alma mater, there on a corporate pass. He spent more time talking to me, beers in hands, than watching the game. To my right, Chris watched the game in a chemical stupor, staring straight ahead, not moving a twitch, as if a metal rod connected his head to the rest of his body, like a Sicilian puppet. When it was all over, he rose from his seat and said flatly, "I loved it."

The plane trip home was blessedly uneventful. Chris was overjoyed to be back in Geneva with his family. Within two days, his rusty vocal cords began to get some use. He was talking more. Not much, but more.

Now that he was at home, the big question on all our minds was: "What's next?"

Doctor Piaget told us about an outpatient day program associ-ated with the Hôpitaux Universitaires de Genève that focused on intervention at the prodromal (before the onset of acute symptoms) and first-episode phases of schizophrenia. The city-wide program, referred to by its French acronym HOPE,* was overseen by "Doctor Rx,"

---

* Not the real name of the program

an eminent psychiatrist and psychopharmacologist, and was open to young adults between the ages of eighteen and twenty-five. The clinic closest to us operated out of an office building that was twenty minutes from our apartment, on foot, and was run by another psychiatrist, Doctor Tissot.

HOPE sounded promising to Ian and me, so we asked Doctor Piaget to find out if there was a waiting list or what we needed to do to enroll Chris. We were heartened to learn that a space would open up soon. Adding to our good fortune, we learned that our medical insurance would cover the full cost.

While he waited to begin the program, Chris stayed cooped up in our apartment. Agitated, he paced around the dining room table at frequent intervals throughout the day. Eyes half closed and drooling slightly, he circled round and round.Occasionally, he sat down and plucked out a few notes on his guitar. Then he would put the guitar down and get up to resume his familiar pattern of laps. The rest of us took turns shouting at him to sit down and at least try to enjoy whatever television show we were watching, but round and round he went, oblivious to our pleas.

I wasn't sure if the pacing was a symptom of Chris's illness or if the drugs were causing a simultaneously zombie-like and manic condition. I had witnessed similar behavior at CAMH. Shouldn't Chris have improved by now? I worried that maybe he was regressing.

At Easter, when traffic clogged the highways heading south to France and Italy, our family headed north to Germany for what had become an annual trip to the spa town of Baden-Baden.Our first evening there, Chris and I went for a walk near the guest house where we were staying. Suddenly, and without explanation, he stopped, hesitated for a moment, and then turned around and headed toward the guest house. I started to run after him, and then I realized what was happening. He was hearing voices.

I stood in front of him and asked, "Are you hearing voices?"

He avoided looking me in the eye. "Yes," he mumbled. "The voices are telling me to go back."

In the brief time I'd spent with the doctors at CAMH, the subject of auditory hallucinations was never raised. I had assumed that either Chris didn't hear voices or the drugs had silenced them. I was wrong.

"Chris," I said heatedly, "tell the voices to take a flying leap. Tell them that they are not real!"

My naïve advice came not from medical professionals but from watching *A Beautiful Mind*.

I put my arm around Chris and slowly walked with him back to the guest house, fearful that he might suddenly bolt, the way he had at the donut shop in Toronto. I needn't have worried; he followed meekly. But this new realization troubled me. If Chris was taking medication, why was he hearing voices? I was glad that he would soon be entering a highly regarded program geared toward early intervention, and hopeful that the doctors at HOPE could heal him. They would surely know what to do about the voices.

At the end of May, Chris, Ian, and I met with Doctor Rx in his office and learned more about the HOPE program. Chris would attend the program from 9:00 a.m. to 3:00 p.m. five days a week for four to eighteen months, depending on his progress. He and others in his cohort would receive individual and group therapy, music therapy, art therapy, drama therapy, and cooking lessons. They would be supervised by staff social workers, psychologists, psychiatrists, occupational therapists, and nurses. The aim was to help participants reintegrate back into the community—and to prevent relapses. Every second Tuesday, from 12:30 p.m. to 1:45 p.m., family members were invited to attend a "family circle" to share experiences, ask questions, and learn more about mental illness.

"As you can see," explained Doctor Rx, "social integration is the principal preventive therapeutic treatment, but we also believe that the judicious use of medication is equally important. We prescribe different kinds of medications, but we have found, in the ten years the program has been operating, that one particular neuroleptic drug, clozapine, seems to be producing especially good results in the patient population."

Chris was set to start the program the following week. Ian and I were enthusiastic when we left Doctor Rx's office. The only drawback we could see was that everyone at HOPE spoke French. We gamely looked at it as a chance to "grow" our French language skills, albeit in a psychiatric context.

Chris, however, wasn't convinced that he needed ongoing treatment, and we had to push him out the door on his first day so he wouldn't be late. Two days later, I received a phone call from one of the nurses, wondering where he was. I wondered too.

I rang the house and Chris answered the phone. To his way of thinking, the program was for "lifers," a category into which he did not place himself. He wasn't budging from his room.

"Get down there, *tout de suite*," I snarled. "Everybody's waiting for you."

He complied.

Later that day, Ian and I confronted Chris about his elitist attitude. Who did he think he was, condemning other kids his age? What made him superior? And how did he think he was going to recover if he refused treatment?

We learned that Chris's plan was to walk around the city and talk to people on the street. How he thought that approach was going to help was a mystery to us—but we did know of a program that was ready and willing to help him. At the very least, the HOPE program would give structure to his days while we were at work. He should appreciate structure, we admonished.

We'd expected that Chris would walk the mile to the program each day, but to ensure he got there on time, Ian and I took turns driving him in the morning on our way to work.

He found his own way home.

Chapter 12

Au Revoir HOPE, Bonjour Belle-Idée ✳

DURING THE MONTH of June, we watched helplessly as Chris slowly deteriorated. He seemed nervous, and as the month progressed, he became more and more disoriented, especially when he left the apartment. As soon as he stepped into the elevator, he assumed the eyes-half-closed "zombie look," a look we rarely saw now when he was inside our apartment. On the streets, he walked very slowly, vigilant for any sign of trouble.

Though his behavior distressed us, my husband and I took comfort in the knowledge that Chris was taking medication for his illness and he was observed every day at HOPE, so we didn't raise our concerns with the staff. We assumed that Doctor Tissot and his team knew how to deal with Chris's symptoms.

When I arrived home from work one evening, Chris was not in the apartment. As I tried to collect my panicky thoughts, the phone rang.

It was the police. Chris had been picked up in the vicinity of the train station because he looked and acted unwell, the officer said. His pants were falling down, and he seemed disoriented.

Taylor accompanied me to the Hôtel de Police, where we were greeted by the officer I'd spoken to on the phone. The three of us walked to Chris's cell. After unlocking the cell door, the officer motioned to Chris that he was free to leave.

I didn't want to alarm Chris, so I acted as if nothing unusual had happened. I didn't bring up the incident again—nor did I report it to Doctor Tissot. I'd heard that the more times a person is hospitalized the worse the prognosis, and I didn't want Chris to end up in the hospital again. He was neither a danger to himself nor to others—he just needed help finding his way. My husband and I expected some ups and downs as part of the process. HOPE was like part-time institutionalization and was all the treatment Chris required, in my judgment.

During this same period, a friend of mine spotted Chris lurking around the Lutheran Church in the Vieille-Ville. Chris rarely talked to me about religion or spirituality, but my instincts told me that he was on a quest to know God. If he was still grappling with religious preoccupations, church was a logical place for him to go. Still, I was deeply distressed to now see my son as the kind of person I had avoided in the past: a lost soul wandering the streets and loitering in churchyards.

At the end of June, I was in Syria on a work-related trip when Doctor Tissot called Ian to express his concerns about Chris's deteriorating behavior. The decision was made to hospitalize Chris for "a couple of weeks" at Belle-Idée, the local psychiatric hospital, while his medication was switched from risperidone to aripiprazole, which had recently become available in Switzerland under the brand name Abilify. (The buzz among the patients and families at HOPE was that Abilify would work wonders for the program's participants.)

I was dismayed by Doctor Tissot's actions. Didn't HOPE aim to prevent relapses that required hospitalization? So why was he now recommending inpatient care?

Starting a new program must have spooked Chris, I concluded. I was beginning to understand his concerns. Being an outpatient meant

Something Was Wrong with Him. Spending his days at HOPE, he couldn't escape the conclusion that he too was a Patient and might become one of those *lifers*.

Despite my confusion and misgivings, I hoped that the Abilify and a stay at Belle-Idée would make Chris well again. I had noticed that when other young people in the group reentered the program after some time at Belle-Idée, they seemed better.

Belle-Idée (which means "beautiful idea") began in an era when gardening and farm work were considered useful in the therapeutic rehabilitation of psychiatric patients. Today, the surrounding farmland is fenced off from the hospital grounds; patients no longer do farm work or tend animals. (Their chief outdoor activity, from what I observed, was smoking.) Situated in a leafy Geneva suburb, a tree-lined street leads to hospital's main entrance. The setting *is* beautiful—green, peaceful, and serene, a striking contrast to CAMH's urban location.

Chris's stay at Belle-Idée lasted much longer than "a couple of weeks"—he was, in fact, there for two months. When he was admitted, Ian and I were tired; we were happy to not have to care for him on a daily basis. His extended absence from our apartment gave us a chance to recover, and his problems moved from the front of our minds toward the back. We needed a break from the constant worry and stress.

Week after week, Ian and I visited the hospital, sitting with Chris in the sunshine in the little forested area near his building. Chris had asked to be taken off Effexor and was only taking Abilify, which may have explained why his ability to engage in conversation was somewhat improved. His face was more relaxed, and he seemed more like his old self. Abilify was okay in Ian's and my opinion—not spectacular, but okay. Any improvement that we saw in Chris's condition was good enough for us.

Apparently, neither Chris nor his doctor at Belle-Idée shared our satisfaction with his meager improvement while taking Abilify. In the doctor's opinion, the drug was not working. He wanted to keep Chris on a low dose of Abilify and also start him on clozapine* (the

---

* Clozapine is available in the U.S. under the brand name Clozaril.

drug that Doctor Rx had claimed was so impressive when we met with him). Ian and I objected, partly because we were happy enough with the slightly more responsive Chris that we were beginning to see and partly because we had read that clozapine is the drug of last resort. The literature we'd read described clozapine's usefulness for treatment-resistant schizophrenia. I refused to believe that Chris was "treatment-resistant." I believed that we just had not yet found the treatment that would work for him.

Chris's doctor assured us that clozapine was not a drug of last resort, but I wasn't convinced. We remained at an impasse for several weeks.

Judging from casual remarks I overheard while attending the family circle, I concluded that many patients at HOPE were given clozapine. Sold in Switzerland under the brand name Leponex, clozapine is the only neuroleptic manufactured by Novartis, a Swiss company formed in the 1996 merger of two Swiss chemical–life science companies, Sandoz and Ciba-Geigy. Was it merely a coincidence that the staff at the HOPE program favored a drug produced by a Swiss company? I wondered.

When taking clozapine, regular blood draws are necessary to monitor white blood cell count. A drop in granulocytes (a type of white blood cell) can lead to frequent chronic bacterial infections of the skin, lungs, throat, et cetera—a potentially fatal condition called agranulocytosis. The prospect of a lifetime of regular blood draws for Chris was unacceptable to me. Nonetheless, Ian and I agreed to give clozapine a try.

The doctors at both HOPE and Belle-Idée said that they typically prescribe neuroleptics at low doses. This conservative approach to the administration of psychiatric medication is commonly found in Europe, they told us. (An average dose of clozapine might be 100 to 150 mg in Europe, compared to, say, 400 to 600 mg in North America.) Chris's doctors also favored pairing a primary low-dose neuroleptic, such as Abilify (aripiprazole), with a second low-dose neuroleptic, such as Leponex (clozapine).

To Ian and me, the minimal-dose approach seemed sensible, but I was skeptical about adding a second neuroleptic. I thought that a single drug, if it does what it is touted to do (stop psychosis), should be sufficient. If it isn't effective, change the drug; don't introduce the risk of more side effects by adding more drugs. This multidrug approach seemed highly unscientific, a random trial-and-error strategy launched with the hope of stumbling upon the right combination.

Chris's new regimen, combining low doses of both Abilify and Leponex, did not result in any noticeable improvements as far as I could see. He still did not mingle with the other patients, and he gained even more weight. (He'd gained fifty pounds after being put on neuroleptics at CAMH.)

"Chris, can't you make friends with the others?" I begged him.

No; the patients at Belle-Idée were lifers. He was different. Secretly, I hoped he was right.

With Chris not responding well to treatment, Ian and I searched for reasons why he had developed schizophrenia in the first place. Had our occasional conflicts and arguments had a negative impact on our sensitive firstborn child? Had Chris shown evidence of a predisposition to schizophrenia from an early age and we'd missed it?

As I wondered what possible precursors could have gone unrecognized during his early life, the ten-month silent pregnancy was the first thing that came to my mind. Were there other factors in Chris's upbringing or childhood that contributed to his later break with reality?

Burdened by unanswered questions, I undertook a thorough review of the landscape of Chris's life before the crisis. I knew I couldn't change the past, but maybe with awareness I could avoid repeating harmful patterns in the future. Maybe I could change the course of Chris's recovery and overcome my fears. Now was not the time to defend my self-image as mother; now was the time for an honest assessment of what might have gone wrong, as well as what I'd done right. I wasn't looking for something—or someone—to blame, but for something I could change. I thought that if I understood the reasons why Chris had suffered a psychotic breakdown, I stood a better chance of helping him recover.

Chapter 13

❋ Start with Childhood

IAN AND I had been married for less than two years when Chris was born. We lived in an apartment in downtown Ottawa and were both employed by the federal government. To the amazement of my colleagues, I worked right up to the day before giving birth. I'd expected that I would easily settle into being a mother, despite the fact that I had never given babies or motherhood much thought. (I'd never even held a baby in my arms until I held Chris.)

Unlike a lot of other mothers, I didn't read books about what to expect when expecting, although Ian and I did attend a prenatal course. Perhaps Chris's love of music was stimulated in utero on the many evenings when Ian strummed his acoustic guitar and together we sang folk songs.

Chris cried a lot in his first few weeks, which, I assumed, is what babies do. There was another explanation for the crying, however. When I took him for his regular checkups, the pediatrician remarked that Chris was healthy and developing well, except that he should have been gaining more weight. The doctor suggested that, in addition to breastfeeding, I consider feeding Chris formula.

To breastfeeding advocates, the substitution of formula for breast milk is close to child abuse, because bottle-fed babies are supposedly more likely to suffer from allergies, cognitive deficits, and infectious diseases.[1] "What responsible mother would knowingly do this to her child?" was the message I received from the propaganda. Our prenatal course had strongly advised choosing breast over bottle to ensure our child a healthy future. I persevered with breastfeeding only.

After several weeks of Chris crying all night and getting longer rather than fatter, I started to supplement my breast milk with formula. Chris began to meet his benchmarks for weight, and our nights were quieter.

When I returned to work after four months of maternity leave, Ian and I hired an energetic middle-aged woman named Norma to come to our apartment every day to look after Chris. My fears about leaving him with a stranger subsided as we got used to a routine. I could see that Chris responded well to Norma, and she to him.

In keeping with his ten-month gestation period, Chris was an extremely placid baby. He sat quietly in my lap while I read to him. Though his behavior sometimes seemed like indifference, I could sense the presence of an old soul, a kindly soul, a child born with goodwill.

Just as remarkable as Chris's lengthy gestation period was his strong constitution. He was never ill as a baby or as a child—not even a cold or a fever.[2] This imperviousness to everyday illness carried on through his teenage years and into adulthood. (Chris is a lot like his father in this regard.)

Chris was a late walker but an early talker. At eighteen months, he knew all of his numbers and letters and proudly recited them. When he was two, he stopped on the sidewalk one day after noticing a dandelion growing through a crack in the pavement. "Pretty flower," he said sweetly. He told our neighbor, "That's a Beatles song on the radio, Sherry."

Because of his precocious vocabulary, thoughtfulness, and gentle nature, Ian and I imagined that Chris was a deep thinker. We used to joke about the contrast between "the thinker" and "the doer." Alex was the "doer." Born two and a half years after Chris, Alex was action-oriented—even in the womb. Sitting on my lap held no attraction for him. He wanted off immediately to go prod the world with a stick. No "pretty flower" observations for Alex. He uttered his first sentence in our car, lunging toward the steering wheel: "Car car drive it!" (I believe Alex thought he should be doing the driving rather than Ian.)

After Alex was born, Ian built a large sandbox in our backyard. (We'd bought a house in a suburb of Ottawa.) Alex would show up at the back door covered in sand and water from the garden hose that had mysteriously found its way into the sandbox, but Chris remained as clean as a dove, as if he had hovered over the sandbox but never gotten into it.

When the "doer" entered a room, the tension level changed perceptibly; it felt as if an electric current crackled through the room and everyone in it. The "thinker" on the other hand, quietly floated into the room, unseen and unheard. Without warning, Chris's sudden presence was unsettling to those he appeared beside. Unlike the "doer," who hated to go to bed, Chris put himself to bed at night. He would suddenly disappear and I'd find him waiting for his tuck-in, ready to call it a day. *Yup,* I'd think, *definitely an old soul.*

Chris's otherworldly presence, I am convinced, started the moment he was conceived. That pinging sound I heard—could it have been a harp string? I'm half joking, but whatever it was, that sound seemed to signal that a highly spiritual being was entering our lives.

Marriage and children tested everything about Ian and me that we wrongly thought we were mature enough to handle. We argued a fair amount during our early years together. We were locked in an eternal power struggle, each trying to turn the other into someone more like ourself.

When our arguments got too heated, Chris would put his little hands over his ears and take a step backward, looking as if he was about to cry. Invariably, Ian and I would make up on the spot, scoop Chris up in our arms, and sing silly songs while parading around the apartment, Chris riding high on Ian's shoulders.

As our family grew, we had to adjust to two more distinct personalities in the household. Taylor was born three years after Alex. We referred to him as "the designer" because he had a strong sense of personal style. Like the stereotypical youngest child, he was easygoing; Alex, the middle child, was the one who tested Ian's and my patience to the limit. Unlike Chris or Taylor, Alex got yelled at and spanked. It took us years to learn how to work with him. (The key, we eventually discovered, was to just let him have his way.)

In short, ours was a fairly noisy household when our sons were young, and our interactions were not always harmonious. I regret that I didn't have more control over my temper back then.

Chris's suburban boyhood passed unobtrusively and a bit mechanically, due to his lack of physical energy and his dutiful nature. Like his younger brothers, he joined the Cub Scouts, attended Sunday School, played soccer (the usual position for all three boys was goalie), and learned to skate and ski.

Our house was always filled with little boys from our immediate neighborhood, so I didn't worry about whether Chris had enough friends or whether he was a bit too passive. In an active household, we didn't have the luxury of focusing on any one child unless there was real cause for concern. Concerns are usually associated with "bad" children; they are the squeaky wheels that continually demand grease. People rarely notice that the "good" child might be struggling, especially if he's doing okay in school.

Alex was the squeaky wheel in our family, and we sent him to a psychologist when he was eleven. The intervention came about as a result of what I call "the white van syndrome." This is the fear (rational or irrational, depending upon your perspective) that overtakes mothers who listen to too many "white van" stories (it's invariably a white van) about child abductions or near abductions, or just the fact that a white van was reported driving around their neighborhood. Parents then impose a lockdown. No longer can children walk the few blocks to school; they must be personally escorted or driven. They must let their parents know where they are at all times.

Alex was not responding well to my need to know where he was and what he was doing. Our conversations quickly became shouting matches. The psychologist concluded that Alex was like Huckleberry Finn. The sooner Ian and I appreciated his strong desire for independence, the better. We got the message. Alex got a bus pass as soon as we moved to Geneva. We encouraged him to light out for the territories and "come home when you're done."

Perhaps we should have taken Chris to a child psychologist as well, though I wonder how seriously a mother would have been taken when complaining about a seemingly perfect child. Chris wasn't terrorizing the neighborhood or failing in school. After many attempts to teach him to be more assertive, I gave up trying to change his self-effacing, permission-seeking, and apologetic tendencies. I instinctively knew that something would eventually happen that would cause him to change. I just didn't know the "something" would be a schizophrenic breakdown.

By the age of ten, Chris was taller and heavier than most of the boys his age. (I thought he would naturally shed his excess pounds as he grew older and taller. I was fat at that age too.) If he was picked on he kept it to himself, except for the day he came scurrying home from the park, clearly panicked. After locking the doors, closing the windows, and shutting the blinds on the patio doors, he cautiously peered outside. I asked him what was going on, and he told me not to worry. "Just a bunch of boys ganging up on me."

It was an isolated incident, so I didn't inquire further. Being bullied seemed like one of those inescapable childhood experiences. I figured my sons would learn how to stand up for themselves. Moreover, no boy wants his mother interfering on his behalf; doing so could invite more humiliation from peers.

One of Chris's friends had recently introduced him to a fantasy trading card game. Chris was fascinated by the game, and the two boys played it nearly every day after school. Its complexity required the use of strategic decision-making skills. Though Chris probably didn't realize it, the pastime introduced mathematical principles such as probability, statistics, and game theory in a competitive format. (I suspect that the intricate graphic designs on the cards also fired Chris's imagination.)

Some people consider stories and games with magic spells to be evil or satanic, but I figured that Chris would eventually outgrow his interest in the game the way children outgrow fairy tales and Santa Claus. He did not lose interest in the game, however, and as he got older he grew increasingly attracted to science fiction and mythology.

Like a lot of naïve parents, my husband and I eagerly awaited the start of school. We looked forward to helping our sons with their homework and teaching them what was expected of them. We were gradually disabused of that notion. Taylor and Alex weren't receptive to our help, and Chris didn't need it.

Not one of our sons stood out academically in their early years, when we were living in Ottawa. At parent–teacher meetings, Taylor's and Alex's grade school teachers repeatedly asked Ian and me to make sure that the boys did their homework. (Chris stayed under the radar with his teachers because he wasn't a problem student.) We approached these meetings with trepidation, knowing that we got failing marks in the eyes of the teachers because our sons were not performing, and, therefore, we must not be working hard enough to bring about the desired changes in their behavior.

The teachers would invariably offer us a number of tips about how to encourage Taylor and Alex to do their homework. We were told the usual stuff—dedicate a special spot for homework, make sure they have all the materials they need at hand, reward them with gold stars, et cetera. It was all good advice, in theory. It just didn't work in practice. Alex couldn't sit still for more than five seconds, and Taylor would just sit there, like a dead battery. "Helping" deteriorated into nagging and failed to produce results. I gave up. If our sons didn't complete their assignments, they would have to face the consequences. I saw no point in turning our precious evenings into a battle zone.

When Taylor was in the third grade, a psychologist (who later became a good friend of ours) approached Taylor's teacher at the

International School of Geneva and asked if she could do some testing on one of the students as part of her dissertation research. The teacher recommended Taylor because she thought he was an interesting, dreamy child who wasn't living up to his potential.

"Sure," Ian and I agreed, "why not test him?" Little did we know how complicated our lives would become.

The psychologist tested Taylor and found him bright and creative, but she thought he needed help staying focused on his schoolwork. She told us to find a dedicated spot where Taylor could do his homework and to have plenty of paper, pencils, and erasers on hand.

We'd tried some of these suggestions before, unsuccessfully. The psychologist did have some new ideas ("give him a timer") and, in the spirit of goodwill, we tried them. (Taylor's classroom teacher suggested getting his eyes tested. For a brief period, Taylor had a pair of glasses—two pairs, in fact. I never saw him wear them.)

Taylor was in the fifth grade when the school principal called me to a meeting with the school psychologist to discuss his classroom performance. To my surprise, both the psychologist and the principal were of the opinion that Taylor needed to be on Ritalin because he had Attention Deficit Disorder (ADD). I had some knowledge about ADD from my experience in the Canadian school system, where so many boys who couldn't sit still in class were given Ritalin.

"Ritalin?" I asked, incredulous. "He's hardly hyperactive."

"He's a smart boy, but he's not living up to his potential," said the psychologist. The principal nodded vigorously in agreement.

I left the meeting after promising that I would look into the matter further. I returned home and immediately went online and ordered a book on ADD. When it arrived, I read through it but came away puzzled. Taylor didn't seem to fit the profile.

"Do you see Taylor in this checklist, Ian?"

"No, I don't."

"So what are they on about?"

"Beats me."

Ian and I expressed our reservations at a follow-up meeting with the psychologist and the principal.

"We appreciate your concern," I said, "but we did some research. We don't think Taylor has ADD, so we don't see any reason for him to be on Ritalin."

"He only meets, at most, two of the ten criteria on an ADD checklist we found," Ian added.

The psychologist looked stunned, and the principal swooped in to defend the psychologist's judgment. "Well, you are, of course, entitled to your opinion," said the principal, folding her arms and giving us a frosty look. "But it will be a real shame if this child doesn't live up to his potential."

"That's ridiculous!" said our psychologist friend when Ian recounted the story to her. "Taylor doesn't have ADD. He has no problem focusing on his art projects. He's simply bored with schoolwork."

For the longest time, we feared that the school psychologist and the principal were right about Taylor not Living Up to His Potential. He limped along scholastically for many years. (At one point, his seventh-grade science teacher called us with the grave news that he had simply stopped working, like a broken clock!) Ian and I held out for the magic age of sixteen, when boys are reputed to suddenly pick up the slack and become academically ambitious.

It eventually came for Taylor, as it did for his brothers. He began to pull up his academic socks in the last two years of high school. After he started to apply himself, he remarked, "I'm beginning to see the point of schoolwork."

He graduated in the top 10 percent of his class.

Ian and I have had our share of working with psychologists and psychiatrists—enough to know that they are a mixed lot. Alex's psychologist and the psychologist who tested Taylor had given us decent advice, and the issue of medication was never raised. The psychologist at Taylor's school was ill-informed. (And dangerous. She should not have been dispensing medical advice.)

Our move to Switzerland occasioned a shift in Chris's attitude and behavior. At thirteen, he was about to enter high school. He lost weight, got a guitar, and started to take his academic subjects seriously. He quickly developed a close-knit group of friends who were focused on high marks and achievement. Interestingly, most of them had no siblings or were separated from their nearest sibling by more than a decade. One was adopted.

By his second year of high school, Chris was spending his evenings and weekends practicing with his band, portentously named Revelations. He clearly was in his element playing music. He left the singing to the more socially outgoing members of the band, which was a pity, because he had a good voice and sang well on the few occasions he was willing to be heard. When he was sixteen, he helped organize the annual talent show.

Until his last year of high school, Chris had been increasingly outgoing and studious, so my husband and I were unprepared for the change in his behavior when that trend suddenly reversed and he withdrew into a private world.

We couldn't dismiss his schizophrenia diagnosis and need for treatment as easily as we had dismissed the suggestion that Taylor had ADD and needed Ritalin. Chris's erratic behavior worried us, and our fear made us more willing to follow the advice of medical doctors—for a while, at least.

Chapter 14

The Family Circle ✳

IAN AND I resumed our attendance at the family circle when Chris returned to the HOPE program in September 2004 after two months at Belle-Idée. These meetings were attended by staff, patients, family members, and invited guests.

The routine never varied. The circle opened with introductions all around and was usually led by Claude Tissot, M.D.

"Hello, I am Doctor Tissot. Welcome to the family circle. I see a few new faces here today. Doctor Rubli is visiting us from the University of Zurich. Why don't you say a few words about why you are here today, Doctor?"

"Yes, of course. I'm Thomas Rubli, a clinical researcher in cannabis-associated psychosis. HOPE is one of several successful outpatient programs for psychosis in Switzerland. I'm delighted to be here and interested in learning more about how your program operates."

"Thank you, Doctor Rubli," said Doctor Tissot. "It is indeed a pleasure to have you here. The family circle is an important part of how we educate and involve the families of our patients. Let's continue with the introductions."

"Hello, I am Jean-Pierre Odier, a nurse. I'm also in charge of the cooking class."

"Fabrice, patient."

"I'm Jeannette Picard, the occupational therapist."

"Hello, I am Cyril's mother."

"Cyril, patient."

"Hello, I am Chris's father."

"Chris."

And so on around the circle of about fifty people. (Ian and I questioned the wisdom of encouraging people in a recovery program to self-identify as "patients," but our complaint seemed minor in the larger scheme of things.) After the introductions were made, Madame Calvin, the head nurse, took over.

"Would someone volunteer to tell our newcomers about the program?"

Nurse Calvin's request was the cue for patients and parents to look down at their shoes. A painful, prolonged silence always followed. Then, Jules or Christophe would volunteer to give the patients' perspective on the program and tell the group what a typical week was like.

Jules was humorous and entertaining. He was about twenty, and, from the way he told it, had been quite a pothead. (Recreational drug use was forbidden while attending the program.)

Christophe was as engaging as Jules. His mother and father usually attended the meeting together. His mother, however, was often agitated and accusatory. Her pain and anger were apparent. *This woman should try an antidepressant and get a life,* I often thought, although I admit that I enjoyed the drama she brought to the meetings because without her, the family circle was tedious and uninformative.

Once, when a visiting psychiatrist introduced herself, Christophe's mother abruptly stood up and, before walking out, angrily announced to the group that she did not appreciate having the person who originally misdiagnosed her son's illness present in the room. I couldn't fault her there. (Christophe's parents eventually separated, their marriage undoubtedly strained by the family's ordeal.)

After Jules or Christophe finished talking about day-to-day life in the program, Nurse Calvin always asked, "Does anyone wish to say anything?"

People rarely did. Minutes ticked by, followed by more minutes. Eventually, after another stretch of painful, prolonged silence, someone would ask a question. We learned over time which questions were okay to ask and which ones were not okay.

OK questions:

* ✳ "How does clozapine work?"
* ✳ "What causes schizophrenia?"
* ✳ "What kind of transition program is offered after someone finishes the HOPE program?"

Not-OK questions:

* ✳ "My stomach is sore. Might this be a side effect of the drugs I'm taking?"
* ✳ "I've heard good things about hypnosis. Will you consider offering that to participants in the program?"
* ✳ "How about acupuncture? I'd like to see if that would help my son."
* ✳ "Homeopathy?"

The last fifteen minutes of the family circle were usually spent discussing how a patient transitions out of the program.

"When patients are ready," Nurse Calvin explained, "they can enroll in a sheltered program and learn new skills that will help them integrate back into the community." Then she would trot out some of HOPE's success stories. "Christophe is helping out at a bakery, for example, and Jules is making pottery. Gabrielle is working part-time in an office."

Hearing about the transition period made me fear for Chris's future. He had been enrolled at university, and Ian and I hoped that eventually he would return to his studies and earn a degree.

I wasn't ready to think about a sheltered program for him. How long would he be helping out at a bakery, or some similar task, before he could be back in a degree program? With a sinking heart, I wondered if the staff at the HOPE program discouraged graduates from going to university, believing their patients were incapable of academic achievement.

In any case, Chris wouldn't be resuming his studies any time soon. From what I saw of his behavior at the family circle, it was clear to me that he was not going to quickly exit the program after the required minimum of four months, as Ian and I fervently wished.

Like several of the other young men I saw at the weekly gathering, Chris sat in his chair with his eyes half closed, barely speaking above a whisper. I knew that zombie look from our experience at CAMH. By December 2004, Chris was wearing the same clozapine smile that I had noticed on the faces of some of the other young adults in the HOPE program. It is kind of a stifled smile, as if the patient is enjoying a private joke.

Surely this is related to the drugs he's on, I thought as I glanced around the room. I knew the drugs were responsible for all the weight he had gained. We'd replaced his entire wardrobe three times that year, and his shoulders sagged from the extra pounds he was carrying.

The HOPE program was designed with the aim of providing treatment at an early stage so that the participants would have functional lives outside of an institution, but I wanted more for Chris than just "functioning." I wanted him to thrive.

Were my aims unrealistic, or was I, even then, able to see a more hopeful future for my son than the staff at HOPE could envision?

Chapter 15

If Psychiatrists Ruled the World ✳

IN JANUARY 2005, we celebrated Chris's twenty-first birthday. Time was moving on, and I was losing faith that promising new treatment breakthroughs would appear on the horizon. I started exploring the vast resources available on the World Wide Web.

Online tools for social networking were scarce at that time. (Facebook would be launched later that year.) I'd heard about chat rooms, but had not yet participated in one. For months, I'd simply been typing the words "schizophrenia hope" into my computer's search engine.

I was looking for an organization dedicated to helping people with schizophrenia, but most of the websites that I found were linked to pharmaceutical products or sponsored by pharmaceutical companies; therefore, the desirability of prescription drug use was implicitly accepted—and actively promoted.

According to these sites, the search for better drugs to manage or cure schizophrenia was underway; until then, staying on the prescribed course of meds and following "doctor's orders" was the best advice the World Wide Web had on offer.

My search eventually led me to the website for the National Alliance on Mental Illness (NAMI), which claims to be "America's largest grassroots organization dedicated to improving the lives of persons living with serious mental illness."[1] The message I got from NAMI's website was that the treatment of schizophrenia presents a challenge over the course of a lifetime; for "most people," there was little chance that the symptoms would ever completely disappear:

> Most people with schizophrenia contend with the illness chronically or episodically throughout their lives, and are often stigmatized by lack of public understanding about the disease.[2]

Too many of NAMI's resources seemed to be directed at fighting stigma, an approach I thought was misguided. (Why not focus on empowering recovery? No mental illness, no stigma.)

The organization recommended the widely acclaimed *Surviving Schizophrenia* by E. Fuller Torrey, MD, a book that had been suggested by the team at CAMH in Toronto (despite their general advice to not read too much about schizophrenia).

Although the author has impressive credentials and is considered an authority on schizophrenia, I read only the first chapter or two of his book before deciding that it wasn't for me. Doctor Torrey's attitude toward his patients (whom he refers to as "consumers") seemed clinical and chilly. He didn't seem to have much respect for them; worse, he seemed to consider them lost causes. Suppressing symptoms seemed to be the goal, whether that was through medication or, if needed, electroconvulsive (electroshock) therapy.

I was struggling to stay positive about Chris's future prospects, casting about in a sea of negativity. Some of the best-known names in the field of mental health confirmed my worst fear: *there was no cure for schizophrenia.* The best Chris could hope for (as indicated by Torrey's title) was "survival." If I'd adopted the conventional wisdom and accepted that my son would never get well, I'd have abandoned all hope.

I thought of the doctors in Toronto, who had expected scientific breakthroughs to appear within "five to ten years." Ten precious years in a young person's development, lost? I wasn't willing to wait for some new drug that might or might not be effective—or even safe. My son was not a science experiment.

Night after night, Chris was at home with us. This was no life for a young man. Chris needed to recover *now*. He needed to get on with his life—get back to university, have a girlfriend, get a job. He was lonely. I was lonely for him. His friends had drifted away; they were now in their third year of university somewhere. His brother Alex would be starting university in the United States within a year.

Given the information that was available to me—from NAMI, the HOPE program, and the World Wide Web—I had little reason to expect a positive outcome. Friends and acquaintances who had dealt with schizophrenia in their own families were always saddened by the experience. Their relatives, if still alive, were not well. The newer drugs on the market might offer Chris the relief that had eluded their relatives decades earlier, they suggested. "The medications are so much better these days. It is important to stay on the medications," they would say, repeating the advice of the pharmaceutical companies, the psychiatric profession, and NAMI.

The longer Chris was on the drugs, and the longer he stayed at HOPE, the more he began to look like a chronic patient—the opposite of someone with a treatable condition. Recovery from a cold doesn't drag on; it doesn't require "expert help." I understood that Chris's diagnosis was more serious than the common cold, but I wondered if the drugs and all the medical attention helped keep him in patient mode longer than necessary. The combination spelled "chronicity" to me.

Doctor Tissot did not come out and say that Chris's condition was, in all likelihood, chronic, but his grave attitude toward Chris, Ian, me, and schizophrenia conveyed a sadness that was contagious. I had definitely caught it, and it seemed to have affected others in the family circle.

No doubt Chris also picked up on the sadness, thereby giving Doctor Tissot good reason to see him as a chronic case. Chris was quiet and withdrawn; he didn't join in activities as much as some of the other patients in the program did. But not all of the patients were suffering from schizophrenia; the program was open to young adults with psychological difficulties that had a psychotic component. I suspected that many were there for depression, bipolar disorder, and drug-induced psychosis. Increasingly, I questioned the usefulness of a one-size-fits-all approach to treatment, and comparing Chris's progress with that of other participants only depressed me.

The Chris I knew at home, though far from acting normal, at least communicated with us. He seemed happy to be around us. He talked. Admittedly, he had many peculiarities. I had no way of knowing if these were side effects of the drugs or symptoms of his illness. For the longest time, I thought that what I was seeing was the illness. Over time, it dawned on me that some of his symptoms were caused by the medications he was taking. (Along with his unkempt personal appearance, the appearance of his signature and handwriting changed, and he started writing in large, childish letters. I now believe his fine motor skills were impaired.)

Another peculiarity that I had assumed went hand in hand with a disease state was the popping sound Chris made with his lips, followed by whistling sounds. I decided to raise the issue at one of our private meetings with Doctor Tissot.

"Thank you for bringing your important clinical observations to my attention," Doctor Tissot said. "I'll discuss the matter with my assistant, Doctor Hublot."

Despite this apparent willingness to take my concerns seriously, I noticed the doctor's jaw tighten ever so slightly. My sense was that he thought I was attempting to undermine his authority in these matters by asking questions. Or perhaps, understandably, he didn't want to upset Chris by calling attention to his quirks.

It dawned on me one day, long after Chris had stopped doing it, that what I'd thought of as "popping" sounds could be the "smacking" sounds that are symptomatic of tardive dyskinesia, a serious condition that the literature said often manifested when antipsychotic drugs were taken for long periods of time.[3]

I could see that Chris badly needed his confidence boosted, so he and I secretly resumed the driving lessons he had abandoned two years earlier, when his illness was as yet undiagnosed. Ian would have gone ballistic, had he known. *Best not to tell him*, I decided. I drove Chris out to the countryside on a few occasions and handed him the car keys. He was a good, careful driver, despite being in a fog of medication.

I told Doctor Tissot about the driving lessons, my attempt to show him that the Stand-in-a-Corner-Chris he saw at the day program was not the only Chris. He was not amused. He told me to drop the driving lessons, fast.

"Don't you see this is dangerous?"

I was, apparently, failing to face the cold, hard, depressing reality of Chris's situation. And so, the driving lessons came to a screeching halt.

My husband and I had different ideas about the value of psychiatric intervention; as a result, we often disagreed about what treatment approaches were best for Chris, especially where medication was concerned.

Ian was receptive to the benefits of psychiatry. Early in our marriage, a psychiatrist had helped him see that his mild obsessive-compulsive tendencies could be used as fuel for high achievement. After years of marriage, and after all we had been through with Chris, I began to see the value of this advice. (Ian often dialogues out loud to himself as his way of working out problems with other people and charting future plans of action. He is a prolific author and has written several books as well as many articles for academic journals—all of which were meticulously edited before they ever reached the publisher.)

Given my family background, my distrust of Chris's psychiatrists was probably inevitable. My parents, like many of their friends in the 1950s and 1960s (my formative years), were of the opinion that seeing a psychiatrist only caused people to lean on the psychiatrist, instead of figuring things out for themselves. Bright people tended to be unstable people, to my family's way of thinking, and they were often found in the ranks of the dangerously overeducated.

When we disagreed about the value of the psychiatric treatment Chris was receiving, I reminded Ian that none of *my* relatives had ever been hospitalized for a psychiatric disorder, or, with one exception (dyslexia), had ever seen a psychiatrist. He, in turn, suggested that seeing a shrink might have done me, and my entire family, some good!

Ian and I loved each other, but managing Chris's problems and constantly interacting with mental health professionals was wearing us down. Our social life was beginning to suffer under the strain. We were no longer in the mood to host the parties we had once enjoyed, preferring to get together one-on-one with close friends. Monthly lunches with Pastor Bill Strehlow from our church helped us tremendously during this period.

We also met occasionally with Doctor Piaget, the psychologist we had initially consulted about Chris, whom I was now reluctantly taking on board as the newest member of our extended family of licensed professionals.

"Dealing with psychiatrists," I said during one of our sessions, "is like having an interfering grandmother telling you how to run your household."

We all laughed, but I was dead serious.

Lessons learned in the year following Chris's diagnosis could be summed up as follows:

* Schizophrenia is a very serious chronic disease;

* Psychiatrists, overseeing other professionals, are the people best equipped to manage it;

* Families will cope better with the situation if they get together periodically with other families that are going through a similar experience;

* Patients with different diagnoses and symp- toms get the same drugs;

* Clozapine is a "miracle drug";

* Mental illness is dreary (no upside).

My husband and I had enthusiastically enrolled Chris in the HOPE program. We'd been stalwart attendees at the family circle and monthly meetings with Doctor Tissot because we believed that family support was an important part of the healing process. We showed up, but only learned about the treatment of mental illness from a clinical standpoint. "Participation" translated into "compliance"; deviations from the established program were not encouraged, and I was interested in trying something different, for, as time wore on, I began to doubt the whole approach of this early intervention program. I didn't see any evidence that attending HOPE would ever resolve Chris's psychosis. Managing symptoms with pharmaceutical drugs, combined with scheduled activities to occupy patients' time, did not add up to effective "treatment" in my mind. Too little attention was paid to the side effects of those drugs (both dangerous and merely inconvenient or annoying), or to assisting families of patients so they could become active participants in patients' *recovery*.

I would have to look elsewhere, I realized. Chris was going nowhere at HOPE.

Chapter 16

✳ Orthomolecular Medicine and Beyond

EARLY IN 2005, I searched for "schizophrenia and hope" and struck gold. "There is hope and schizophrenia can be cured," trumpeted the website of the Optimal Life Center.[1] I eagerly read on and learned of psychiatrist Abram Hoffer, MD, PhD and his groundbreaking research on schizophrenia.

In the 1950s, Doctor Hoffer, together with Humphry Osmond, MD, treated schizophrenic patients in Saskatchewan, Canada, with supplements aimed at correcting the body's biochemical imbalances, an approach termed "orthomolecular medicine."[2]

Hoffer and Osmond hypothesized that adrenochrome, a chemical compound produced in the body by the oxidation of adrenaline, has hallucinatory properties similar to LSD.[3] They suspected that adrenochrome interferes with brain function and that too much sets the stage for the formation of schizophrenia.[4] After studying the metabolism of adrenaline, they prescribed large doses of niacin (vitamin B_3) nd other supplements in hopes of inhibiting the formulation of adrenochrome in their patients.[5]

Although it was highly conjectural, the information made sense to me and provided a reasonable explanation for what might be occurring in Chris's body. The doctors at CAMH had asked whether Chris had been using recreational drugs before he was admitted. The observed behavioral effects are similar.

I immediately ordered *How to Live with Schizophrenia*, the book that Hoffer and Osmond had written for schizophrenics and their families. When it arrived, I read it straight through. I was gratified to read a book that offered practical health advice for people suffering from schizophrenia. Orthomolecular treatment (in particular, high doses of vitamin B_3) was recommended for improving patients' chances of recovery.[6]

I'd been introduced to the benefits of vitamin supplements as a teen when my parents started taking large doses of vitamin C and vitamin E. They strongly believed that their ability to stay active and independent in their later years was a result of taking the vitamins. Through them, I knew about Linus Pauling and the Shute brothers, but I had never heard of Doctor Hoffer and the benefits of the B vitamins. I had also never heard that schizophrenia could be cured, or that recovery could be achieved through vitamin therapy.

Ian and I checked a drug interactions website to make sure the supplements recommended by Hoffer and Osmond[7] would not interfere with Chris's prescribed medication. We didn't find any warnings, so Chris started taking a simplified version of the Hoffer-Osmond protocol on March 1, 2005.[8]

Within a week, Chris's energy and focus improved, as did the texture of his skin. He showed more interest in his surroundings. After several weeks, Doctor Tissot also noticed an improvement and slightly decreased Chris's dosage of clozapine.

I wrote Doctor Hoffer a fan letter and read some of his other books. (He responded by letter, urging me to stay on course.) One book in particular, *Smart Nutrients,* was a wealth of information.[9] When his mother was in her sixties, Hoffer wrote, early signs of memory loss and dementia vanished soon after she started the niacin therapy. Swelling in her finger joints also disappeared.

This story hit home for me. My mother developed dementia in

her late seventies. Several years earlier, she had begun complaining about her enlarged knuckles. (She could no longer wear her rings.) How I wish I had known about niacin's anti-inflammatory properties at that time.

I was sold on the benefits of niacin and started taking the same vitamins I was giving Chris. My energy level and my ability to focus improved significantly. (At fifty-three, my mind had begun delivering wrong words to me. What came out of my mouth was not always what I had intended to say: "Please hand me the iron" instead of "Please hand me the pot," for example. I had put it down to being too uninterested in the mundane, too tired and distracted by managing a busy household to worry about the decline in my cognitive abilities. After taking the supplements, I no longer had that problem. In addition, my hair, which had been thinning, reverted back to its original thickness and showed less gray. My skin developed a smooth texture. I had slowed the aging process.)

This was not the first time that B vitamins had played a role in boosting my overall health. When Ian and I moved to Ottawa as newlyweds, I didn't know many people and had difficulty finding a job. A sense of impending doom overcame me, and I was afraid to go outside. My weight plummeted to 109 pounds on my five-foot-five-inch frame. Alarmed, my mother began making references to pop vocalist Karen Carpenter's struggles with anorexia nervosa, hoping to get me to see that I might be headed down the same path.

The doctor I consulted said I was "borderline" for mononucleosis after a blood test showed an elevated white blood cell count. He told me to come back in a week for a retest.

With a window of seven days to restore my health, I found a recipe for a vitamin B "cocktail" and hurried over to the nearest health food store to load up on brewer's yeast, soy milk, wheat germ, and molasses. With the first glass, I experienced a wonderful feeling of peace and relaxation. I drank three or four glasses of this concoction daily, right up until the appointment to have my blood retested.

"What happened?" the doctor asked when he saw that my white blood cell count had returned to normal.

I waxed enthusiastic about the benefits of B vitamins, but he was not interested in my discovery. (Medical schools don't adequately educate students about nutrition,[10] much less teach vitamin therapy.)

Not long after the mononucleosis scare, I became pregnant with Chris and stopped supplementing my diet with B vitamins. I took other vitamins throughout my pregnancy—and felt great—but in hindsight I wonder if adding vitamin B_3 to the mix could have prevented the onset of schizophrenia that Chris experienced as a teen. Doctor Hoffer had observed that niacin deficiency can be present in several generations of family members. Did a niacin deficiency play a role in my mother's dementia, my anxiety, and my son's schizophrenia?

I eventually told Doctor Tissot about the supplements Chris was taking. He didn't express any interest in knowing the specifics (I e-mailed the list of supplements to him anyway), but at least he did not stand in our way.

As several decades had passed since Doctor Hoffer started using orthomolecular medicine to treat schizophrenic patients, I wondered if other researchers and clinicians had followed his lead and added their own contributions to the field. Surely there were orthomolecular doctors who were up-to-date on the latest advances.

Back to my computer I went. I was determined to locate a licensed medical doctor, preferably a psychiatrist, who employed vitamins and minerals in treating mental illness and who would work with our family in getting Chris off prescription drugs, if at all possible. The generally conservative attitude of the medical doctors in Switzerland meant that I would probably have to look outside the country.

I searched until I found her. The next segment of our healing journey was about to begin.

Chapter 17

✳ *Doctor Erika*

ELAINE ERIKA, MD, is a holistic and integrative psychiatrist located in the United States. She specializes in orthomolecular psychiatry and uses energy medicine and other therapies to help her patients avoid, reduce, or eliminate the need for prescription medications.

Practitioners of energy medicine believe that many illnesses can be remedied by rebalancing a person's energy field.[1] Therapies may utilize either measurable (veritable) energies, such as magnetism, light, and sound, or putative energies that influence subtle energy fields (biofields) but cannot yet be detected through scientific means. Reiki, acupuncture, homeopathy, and prayer are a few of the practices in the latter category that are used to restore health.[2]

Doctor Erika's website claimed that she could assist in the recovery and healing of all psychiatric conditions. I discussed her approach with Ian and Chris, and with their consent I telephoned her. I said that our family would be in her area in August and I would like her to treat Chris. She was dubious that we could maintain a relationship from across the Atlantic, but she was willing to see us. First, however, she wanted to do something called muscle testing on Chris so that she would have the results when she saw him in August. Because

Chris had weak muscle tone as a baby, I agreed that muscle testing would be a good idea.

"It's not what you think," Doctor Erika said. She explained that muscle testing is a kinesiology tool that was developed in the 1960s for tapping into the innate intelligence of the body.

"Our bodies respond to subtle energies, just as an EKG or EEG machine responds to electrical energy. Our minds and bodies can sense the energy of an object through thought or exposure." This would all be demonstrated during our meeting, she told me.

It didn't matter to me that I didn't have a clue what she was talking about. I was eager to do anything that would help Chris move forward.

As requested, I gave Doctor Erika Chris's full name, address, and the current dosages of vitamin supplements and medications he was taking. She didn't need to draw blood samples or even be on the same continent with Chris to access information about his nutritional status using muscle testing. Suspending disbelief, I awaited the results.

A few days later, I received Doctor Erika's report—fourteen pages of detailed information. The muscle testing had revealed that Chris's levels of iodine, chromium, selenium, and boron were low enough to have negative health ramifications. Doctor Erika had also found deficiencies in Chris's amino acids (glutamine, 5-HTP, and tyrosine) and recommended supplementation with L-glutamic acid. Even though he had been taking an omega-3 supplement, Chris had a mild essential fatty acid deficiency. Doctor Erika suggested that he either take higher doses or use a more bioavailable form.

According to the report, some of the foods in Chris's diet depleted rather than strengthened his energy field and were harmful to him, especially wheat, eggs, and dairy. Even a small amount of refined sugar was enough to disrupt his metabolism. His vitamin status was normal (probably because he was already following the Hoffer-Osmond protocol), but he had candidiasis, a systemic overgrowth of the yeast-like fungus *Candida albicans*.[3]

Doctor Erika's orthomolecular approach to treating nutritional deficiencies required using specially formulated nutrient-dense supplements that are highly absorbable and bioavailable. (The manufacturing process, I learned, often removes a lot of the nutrients from vitamin and mineral products.)

I telephoned Doctor Erika to find out more about some unfamiliar concepts and terms in her report. *Bioavailability*, she told me, refers to the amount of the nutrient that can be broken down, absorbed, and used by the body. Incomplete absorption can result if supplements are not being properly metabolized by the liver.

"The form in which the nutrients are delivered is as important as the amount taken," she explained. "Some individuals might have trouble absorbing nutrients from supplements taken in pill or tablet form, for example. They may do better with liquids and powders."

I was madly writing down everything she was saying.

"Keep in mind that some vitamins are unsafe in high doses, so it's best to work with a qualified practitioner or do a lot of research before taking any product. Herbs are a good example. Just because they are sold over the counter doesn't mean they should be used haphazardly. Care must be used, because if they are having any effect at all, they are altering the body's chemistry. Too much of even a good thing is still 'too much.'"

"Why muscle testing?" I asked.

"Muscle testing allows me to determine the optimal dosage of each supplement for each patient, and my patients have achieved positive outcomes as a result."

Doctor Erika went on to explain that she seldom uses laboratory tests to confirm her findings, but the tests she had ordered (for thyroid status, candidiasis, and so on) had corroborated her results from muscle testing. If there had been a discrepancy, she said she would trust her muscle testing more than the lab report.

Would Chris continue taking his current supplements (niacin, vitamin C, omega-3, etc.) if he started her recommended treatment? I asked.

"If you decide to start Chris on the bioavailable supplements, then he might have to cut back on the supplements he's been taking," she said, "and he would also need to eliminate wheat, eggs, dairy, and sugar from his diet. I'd need to monitor his nutritional status closely. He could start to heal very rapidly, causing him to feel unusually sensitive to the side effects of his medications. "

Withdrawal from medications can cause the gastrointestinal (GI) tract to function poorly, Doctor Erika warned me, and if Chris's GI tract were to shut down, the supplements would stop working and his condition would deteriorate. Engaging the subtle energy fields of the body (through EFT and distance healing)[4] would be important during the withdrawal process. (Some of the energy work could be done long-distance, Doctor Erika thought, but the healing work that she did with her hands would have to be conducted in her office.)

All of this information was provided for only $450 ($275 for the fourteen-page analysis, which was covered by our insurance, and $175 for the detailed follow-up to my questions). In the time I'd spent with psychiatrists, I had never learned so much about what was happening inside Chris's body and how it could impact his mind.

The future was looking brighter.

Chapter 18

❋ Energy Medicine and Vibrational Energy

DOCTOR ERIKA'S DETAILED analysis of Chris's biochemical makeup helped me better understand what was going on with him on a physical level. Chris's psychiatrists had pronounced him mentally ill by observing his behavior, but failing to test him for underlying medical conditions seemed unscientific to me. Where was the evidence of a biochemical imbalance affecting his brain?

Energy medicine didn't exactly seem scientifically based, either. Putting my faith in Doctor Erika's methods required a huge suspension of disbelief on my part. Still, of the two approaches (conventional and unconventional), I was more willing to trust Doctor Erika's because it fanned within me a flame of hope—hope that she could help us find a solution to Chris's problems, hope that we could be active participants in the healing process, hope that the mystery surrounding schizophrenia, and the sadness I had been experiencing, might begin to dissipate.

Ian and I met with Doctor Tissot and informed him that we intended to work with Doctor Erika. We sought his cooperation and support. Would he be willing to work with us in a collaborative way, taking Doctor Erika's recommendations into account when prescribing medications for Chris? We believed in the HOPE program's approach, we said, but we thought Chris would progress more rapidly if his nutritional needs were also addressed.

We left the meeting with Doctor Tissot's agreement to cooperate with Doctor Erika "as much as possible."

In August 2005, the whole family flew to Toronto. We rented a minivan and checked into a hotel downtown, near Trinity College.

One of the first stops we made was to the Student Accessibility Services office at the University of Toronto to find out how to get Chris enrolled again as a student. (He wasn't ready to resume his studies, but we hoped he would be, someday.) Chris's petition for reinstatement would need to include certification from CAMH that he was suffering from a psychiatric illness at the time he was hospitalized. The request would be reviewed by an appeal board.[1]

After visiting family in the Toronto area, we drove to Washington, D.C. and deposited Chris and Taylor with our good friend Betsy, a former neighbor in Geneva. Ian and I then drove across Pennsylvania and Ohio to Indiana, where Alex was about to begin his first year at Purdue University. Then, we reversed direction and drove back to D.C., picked up Taylor and Chris, and headed to our appointment with Doctor Erika.

It was a beautiful, sunny afternoon when our car pulled into the parking lot in front of Doctor Erika's office, which was located in a suburban strip mall. Little could we have imagined at that moment the extent to which the mainstream medical views that we had accepted were about to be shaken.

Doctor Erika opened the front door and greeted us warmly. I judged her to be about forty-five years of age. Dressed in earth tones, which complemented her dark hair and olive skin, her attire was casual but conservative and seemed appropriate for a psychiatrist.

After a round of introductions, the four of us followed Doctor Erika to an office behind the reception area. She told us about the evolution of her practice and confessed that while working as a pediatric psychiatrist in a major hospital, she had begun to doubt what she'd been taught about serious mental illness. In particular, she questioned the expectation that, with rare exceptions, lifelong treatment with psychiatric drugs was necessary for people like Chris. Now, she was able to see her patients get well, and that was rewarding.

"I enjoy what I'm doing, partly because I continue to learn so much from my patients and their families. I believe that a psychiatrist's role and privilege is to be the patient's advocate for mental health and that physicians have a duty to find efficacious treatments with the least potential for harm, even if that means veering outside the boundaries of mainstream medicine."

Ian and I were delighted to have found a doctor who was willing to challenge conventional thinking about mental illness. During the course of the afternoon, we would learn a lot about Doctor Erika's beliefs.

"I believe that physicians need to educate themselves and their patients about effective methods of healing. Sometimes, that means abandoning long-held views," she said. "We have to stay open to new information and new approaches so we can limit the duration of illness and the cost of treating it. We need to educate patients about prevention, so that they can better maintain health and wellness. Minimizing the use of prescription medications is part of my approach to treatment."

The idea of limiting the duration of illness struck a chord with me; it negated the expectation of chronicity. And getting Chris off psychiatric drugs had been a goal of mine all along. Doctor Erika was speaking my language.

"My plan for today," she said, "is to teach you about the subtle energy field, retest Chris, and then make recommendations on a course of action. I'll start by showing you a video about water crystals."

The video showed what happened when glass jars of untreated distilled water were labeled with words such as "Thank you" or "You Fool" and left overnight. After freezing the water, Japanese researcher Doctor Masaru Emoto photographed the molecular changes that had occurred in the crystals.

The images were amazing. Positive words created beautiful crystals that were symmetrical in shape; negative words produced dull, misshapen crystals. Doctor Emoto claimed that people's intentions influenced the water's structure. Physical distance from the water didn't seem to matter.

"The human body consists largely of water," Doctor Erika said, "so you can see how the vibrational energy contained within thoughts, words, and actions can have an effect on health."

Next, she asked us all to stand while she demonstrated muscle testing, the technique that had enabled her to send us information about Chris's nutritional status. Doctor Erika told us that muscle testing is used by many health professionals.

She asked Taylor to extend an arm and hold it firmly in place while she pushed down on it with her hands. "As you can see," she said, "Taylor is able to resist the pressure I'm putting on his arm. Let's see if he's able to keep his arm steady when I make the following statement: Two plus two equals four."

Taylor did a good job of keeping his arm in place as Doctor Erika continued to apply pressure. Then she told him that "two plus two equals five," and his arm dropped a bit lower.

Doctor Erika repeated this technique with me, using different mathematical statements than she'd used with Taylor. She then asked me two simple questions in Kurdish to test my ability to perceive false statements even when I didn't understand the language. My arm dropped in response to the false statements as my resistance weakened.

"But how can you test someone who isn't in the same room with you?" Ian asked.

Doctor Erika demonstrated her method of testing someone remotely. After making a circle with the thumb and index finger of her left hand, she inserted the thumb and index finger of her right hand into the circle and tried to force the fingers of her left hand apart while asking a question about a person's state of health. As with the arm test, she was looking for strength or weakness.

"To use these methods successfully, pressure must be applied consistently and the questions must be very specific," Doctor Erika explained. "So I might ask, 'Will this particular substance improve Chris's liver function?' But there are several other ways to test remotely. Some practitioners use a surrogate stand-in, for example."

Doctor Erika told us that she also used muscle testing for determining whether particular foods and products would be beneficial for her patients. She tossed Chris an opaque plastic pouch and said, "Hold this against your body with one hand, and hold out your other arm. I'll push down and you resist." Chris's arm started to sag when Doctor Erica applied pressure.

"Your muscles are having trouble resisting the pressure because you're holding a bag of sugar. Your body knows that this particular substance isn't beneficial. Your arm would remain strong if the bag contained something nutritious."

Doctor Erika took her seat, a cue for the rest of us to sit in our chairs too.

"Thoughts and emotional stimuli produce these same responses, not just physical substances like sugar," she continued. "I could achieve a similar effect by writing the word 'war' on a piece of paper, placing it in a box, and having you hold the box. Or, in your mind, you could imagine something like a family pet. The person doing the testing will know by the way your muscles respond whether thinking about the pet weakens you or strengthens you."

The idea that human consciousness can access knowledge non-locally, across space and time, was mind-blowing.

Throughout the afternoon, Chris remained withdrawn. He didn't look up much and talked so quietly that Doctor Erika had to ask him to repeat himself on more than one occasion. Yet he was paying close attention to what she was saying.

Taylor, on the other hand, was clearly bored. He was polite but distant and uninterested. He would have preferred to be outdoors enjoying the good weather.

I can't say I blamed him. Requiring a fifteen-year-old to spend an entire afternoon of his vacation at a doctor's appointment, on his brother's behalf, was asking a lot. Coping with a child's illness is part and parcel of being a parent, but the sick child's siblings can develop resentment at the disruptions in the household. Everyone's goodwill and patience are tested to the maximum.

The task of assimilating, in one afternoon, all of the information that Doctor Erika gave out was overwhelming, but we still were not done. Next we learned about Emotional Freedom Technique (EFT) and energy visualizations, two mind–body techniques used by professionals who practice energy psychology, a relatively new specialty within the field of psychology. (Energy psychology draws upon psychological interventions (holding specific thoughts) and energetic interventions (techniques that affect the body's meridians[2] and/or chakras[3]) to restore the proper energy flow in our bodies, which can be disrupted by a variety of factors, including illness and trauma as well as our own thoughts and emotions.) Our physical bodies seem solid, but they are made up of atoms that carry positive and negative charges. We are, in essence, bundles of energy. To practitioners of energy medicine, the way we use our energy affects our overall health.

Doctor Erika recommended EFT to help clear blocks from the body's bioenergy system and facilitate healing. When using EFT, the person thinks about a problem or issue and states an affirmation while rubbing her chest in the area of the heart chakra.[4] After identifying the problem, she expresses the willingness to forgive. ("Even though I have this [problem], I deeply and completely love, accept, and forgive myself and all others.") A reminder phrase that focuses on the problem is repeated while the person taps certain meridian points on her body with her fingers.[5]

Doctor Erika led us through several practice rounds of EFT and then showed us a grainy video of Gary Craig[6] in the shallow end of a swimming pool with a man in his fifties. The man had nearly drowned as a child and was afraid to put his face in the water. After using EFT, he was able to submerge his whole body and later took swimming lessons.

Because the process of determining where a trauma lies is a challenge when dealing with complex conditions such as schizophrenia, Doctor Erika explained that she primarily uses EFT with her patients to manage the symptoms that arise during the medication withdrawal process. "I can already see that you are the kind of parents who will be very involved with Chris's recovery," she told Ian and me. "Just don't overdo it, or you may burn yourselves out."

Next, Doctor Erika introduced an energy healing visualization. She told us all to stare at an object in the room for several seconds and then close our eyes.

"Imagine yourself going on a journey. The sun is behind you, warming you. Breathe deeply and allow the tension to melt away. Notice how your body feels with each breath in and out. You are relaxed, happy, enjoying the hot sun on your back. Let's stay with this feeling for a few minutes."

Several minutes went by as the four of us Stayed with Our Feelings. Admittedly, it was a struggle for me to maintain my focus and not let my mind wander.

"Now, see yourself turning around slowly and facing the sun. Step into the sunlight," Doctor Erika instructed us. "Feel the sun's energy flowing into you, becoming one with you. You feel powerful, drawing the healing energy of the sun into your body. You are at one with the universe. Stay with this feeling for a few minutes and then gradually become aware of your surroundings and open your eyes."

I opened my eyes and felt relaxed and at peace. This was the first time I'd ever done guided imagery.

After the tutorial part of the session ended, Doctor Erika was ready to retest Chris's nutritional status. While she muscle tested him in absentia, using her finger technique, the four of us went out for a coffee.

When we returned an hour and a half later, Doctor Erika went through the test results with us and recommended a number of supplements and dietary guidelines. The dietary recommendations were based on a scoring system, with 100 meaning Chris would have no difficulty using, metabolizing, digesting, or absorbing a particular food, and a score of zero meaning a complete inability to use, metabolize, absorb, or digest that food.

Chris's scores in the meat category ranged from a high of 60 (fish and shellfish) to a low of 45 (organic chicken liver). His dairy and grain scores were close to zero. Doctor Erika told him to eat only those foods with a score of 50 and above. That meant switching from cow's milk to soy milk, eliminating eggs, wheat, and sugar, eating pork and fish (or shellfish) but not beef—the list went on and on.

We left Doctor Erika's office with a staggering number of supplements. (In total, we'd purchased about twenty different products—vitamins, minerals, amino acids, and essential fatty acids.) But rather than feeling overwhelmed, I was excited. Now we had a therapeutic approach that we could use to help Chris. No longer would we be at the mercy of his diagnosis. Until Doctor Erika, no one had ever told us there was something we could do to help him get well. I left her office feeling tired to the bone but optimistic. I had a headache. It had been a long day. But now I had some tools.

The clozapine, however, was still a problem. Doctor Erika wasn't sure whether Chris could successfully withdraw from it after taking it for nearly a year. She promised to seek Abram Hoffer's advice on the matter and get back to us.

Several weeks later, she reported that treatment with clozapine can be stopped, but it must be done very, very slowly.

Chapter 19

✳ *Clashing Paradigms*

BACK HOME IN GENEVA, I reorganized the kitchen cupboards to make room for Chris's supplements, which took up a lot of shelf space. To accommodate his new diet, I bought pork (pork roasts, pork chops, pork sausages) because it was one of the few meats that had scored over 50 when Doctor Erika tested him. We ate chicken sparingly, found a dense sunflower seed bread, and consumed lots of smoked salmon.

Chris's appetite for chocolates and sweets had been difficult to control since he'd started taking medication. He hadn't been addicted to sugar in the past, but he was now. He was eating, eating, eating, all the time, and sweets were contributing to his weight problem. He would just go out and buy a chocolate bar whenever he felt like it.

I tried not to get angry about Chris's dietary lapses and the fact that he was putting on so much weight, but maintaining my composure was easier said than done, and I often resorted to nagging. Chris never argued back. He would smile and say, "Oh, okay, I'll try not to eat so much," but his resolve never lasted.

Doctor Erika used EFT affirmations to support him, by phone, in getting rid of toxins. She also encouraged Ian and me to work with him on a daily basis for three weeks, using an affirmation of our choosing.

We focused on Chris's apologetic nature. Ian and I felt better after each session, but we couldn't be sure of the effect on Chris. Overall, he seemed more grounded, enough that we were confident he was ready to take a step forward, perhaps by resuming his studies. We suggested that he consider auditing a course at Webster University, the local English-language university. He would only have to sit in the classroom and listen—no exams, no grades. Chris expressed interest in a political science course that was scheduled to start in October, ending just before Christmas.

The three of us met with Doctor Tissot after Chris had been back in the HOPE program for a week. (Chris had been taking Doctor Erika's recommended supplements and following the new diet for several weeks, and he'd also been practicing EFT while he was away. Ian and I were curious to find out if Doctor Tissot had noticed any changes in his symptoms.) We told Doctor Tissot about our efforts and said we'd observed small improvements in Chris's demeanor. He seemed happier and more relaxed than we'd seen him in a while.

Doctor Tissot did not share our enthusiasm. He had not observed any improvement in Chris's condition. He thought October was too soon for Chris to take a course at Webster but reluctantly agreed to arrange for him to take a few hours off from the program each week to attend classes.

Ian and I were disappointed with Doctor Tissot's response. His opinion still carried a lot of weight with us.

Doctor Erika was accustomed to resistance from other psychiatrists. "They may regard the supplement program as intrusive and unwelcome," she'd warned us.

Having driven a wedge between Doctor Tissot and ourselves with our insistence on trying something new, Ian and I were left to face the consequences. We had to see our plan through and knew we would be looked upon with suspicion and disapproval by the staff at the HOPE program.

But Ian did not oppose the meds as I did, and our difference of opinion was causing tension in our relationship. Ian was willing to try

Doctor Erika's approach if it would allow Chris to flourish without the medications, but he didn't object to Chris taking drugs for the rest of his life if he needed them to function.

In mid-September, I wrote to Doctor Erika to ask her advice. She had told us that a setback was predictable as Chris's body worked to rid itself of toxins, including the prescription meds, but I was scared. Chris had been doing all right—up until about a week before. He had faithfully taken the nutritional supplements as well as the prescribed Leponex (25 mg daily) and Abilify (15 mg daily). Then, he had suddenly become spacey and unfocused, and he stayed that way for long periods of time. He would sit down at the dinner table and stare at his plate. He said he "just didn't feel well," but he couldn't specify why or how.

Doctor Erika promptly followed up with further muscle testing, which indicated that a gradual lowering of the Abilify dosage to 12.5 mg would be helpful but would also produce more symptoms as Chris's body adjusted to regulating certain functions without the aid of medication. Lowering the dosage of a neuroleptic drug often causes anxiety and insomnia and a temporary decrease in self-control, she wrote in her report.

Learning that Chris's recent difficulties could be attributed to his body no longer needing as much medication reassured me that we were on the right track. Our challenge now was to convince Doctor Tissot that Chris's Abilify dosage needed to be lowered. I chose my words carefully and sent the following e-mail:

> Dear Dr. Tissot,
>
> I've been noticing that Chris is having more difficulties lately, such as taking a long time to get dressed in the morning. His speech is slower, too, and he often seems disoriented. I believe that what I'm seeing is the result of introducing the supplements and the energy work as recommended by Dr. Erika. She believes that Chris's need

for prescription drugs is diminishing, as we all hoped would happen. Dr. Erika suggests lowering the dosage of Abilify to 12.5 mg. Ian and I are in agreement with this, as we believe these latest symptoms will clear up when Chris is on a slightly lower dose of the medication.

As always, we very much appreciate the care that Chris is receiving from you and the staff at the HOPE program.

Yours sincerely,
Rossa Forbes

I was astonished by the response I received.

Dear Mrs. Forbes,

Thank you for this information. I would like to briefly answer. Chris is doing less well. My hypothesis is that the approaching start of his course at the university is a stress factor and he is showing active anxiety. In addition, taking into account the clinical observations that we made, our option would be to increase the treatment (Leponex in any case) and not to decrease. We seem to have a paradigm incompatibility, which can also pose a problem for Chris (in whom should he have confidence?). In this context I would like to propose a meeting as soon as possible, even if Mr. Forbes isn't able to be present. I'm available this afternoon at 4 p.m. Is this a convenient time for you?

With my best wishes,
Dr. Claude Tissot

As Chris's mother, I would pit my hypotheses about the reasons for Chris's anxiety against Doctor Tissot's hypotheses any day. Where did he get the idea that Chris was anxious about taking a course at Webster? Did he actually talk to Chris about this?

Chris, despite looking dysfunctional and acting dysfunctional, had told me that he wanted to get back to the patterns of his old life. Doctor Tissot was turning everything about Chris's life into a stress factor, thereby justifying an increase in medication.

That afternoon, I met with Doctor Tissot as he'd requested. He looked at me with his sad, guarded eyes and told me that Chris was "very ill" and that his recovery was going to take a long time. By that, I was sure he meant "never."

Doctor Tissot couldn't fathom how Chris could possibly audit a course at Webster and expressed concern that Chris would be laughed at by the other students. He cautioned me that Chris would never be the "brilliant student" he had once been." (I'd never described Chris as "brilliant"; I'd merely described him as "a good student.")

"Of course, there is always hope," he said, with a lack of conviction, "but please learn to accept the present situation and try to live with it."

What was he getting at? I wondered. That Chris's IQ had dropped?

The depressing information I had read about schizophrenia referred to the tendency for IQ to decrease over time. This statistic is often accompanied by the warning that the longer the delay in starting medication, the greater the decrease in IQ is likely to be. Eventually I came around to the conclusion that this is one of the scare tactics used by the pharmaceutical industry to coerce people into staying on their medication.

Doctor Tissot and I were, indeed, following incompatible paradigms. From my perspective, Chris had difficulty conversing with people, and he had odd mannerisms, but he was intelligent, sensitive, and caring. I refused to believe that he wouldn't be able to cope with auditing a course. I didn't expect him to take a course for credit—not at this stage, anyway. The plan was for him to become reacquainted with being in a classroom by sitting in on a class and doing some of the required reading. Surely he could handle that much, I thought. I believed the drugs were all wrong in Chris's case. They weren't making him better; they were keeping him a psychiatric patient.

I left Doctor Tissot's office on the verge of tears; as I walked home, they flowed freely. Standing up against an institution, alone, was difficult. I felt intimidated by the authoritarian way psychiatrists wielded power. They claimed to understand the brain's biochemistry, and they told people that there was this thing called Serious Mental Illness that only psychiatrists knew how to treat, yet it was becoming clear that their approach did not yield good results.

Chris was fine once; why was he not fine now? People can recover from cancer. Why is mental illness any different? Doctor Hoffer and Doctor Erika didn't believe that schizophrenia was irreversible. Who was Doctor Tissot to write off my son's future?

I wondered if psychiatrists rely upon pharmaceuticals because double-blind studies and statistical analyses sound "scientific." If they cannot hope to cure a condition like schizophrenia, at least they can point to an agreed-upon treatment in the event that something goes wrong—as when a patient commits suicide. The pills they prescribe, given in a standard dosage, provide a measurable formula that can be applied consistently; no independent thought or personal judgment need be employed. If one individual reacts negatively to the treatment, then the problem must lie with the patient, not with the treatment, and certainly not with the treating psychiatrist.

As I trudged along, another depressing thought occurred to me. Was Doctor Tissot concerned that attending a college course would put Chris over the edge?

As far as I knew, Chris had never been suicidal, but I'd read that 5 to 10 percent of the schizophrenia population would commit suicide, usually within five years of onset of the illness. (Doctor Hoffer suggested that the rates would be higher for schizophrenics were it not for the ones who are apathetic.[1] Apathy probably saves a certain percentage from killing themselves; they can't muster the energy!)

I couldn't guarantee that Chris wouldn't kill himself. Ever since he unenthusiastically began the HOPE program, I lived with the fear that I would arrive home one day to find an ambulance pulled up in front of our building because Chris had decided to jump from our sixth-floor balcony.

An unstated fear of suicide, like other unstated fears, wafted like a curl of smoke around the program. You could smell it in the hallways, on the walls, in the private meetings with the doctors. It clung to your clothing and hung in the room during the family circle.

Soon after Chris started at HOPE, one young woman did commit suicide. She'd been in the program for less than a month when she killed herself. We barely knew her. The room went silent when Doctor Tissot, ashen-faced, delivered the news to the family circle.

In the courtyard outside, where the parents gathered after the meetings, the tragedy was not discussed, but a rumor circulated that one of the men who had previously been in the HOPE program was the arsonist behind a recent fire at Belle-Idée. Sad news provokes more talk of sad news.

These unsettling events were not brought into the open by the staff beyond the tersest of announcements. They would be talked about by the families later, in private, at home.

Not being a fluent French conversationalist, I had difficulty forming connections with the other parents and limited my efforts to simple greetings like "Bonjour" and "Ça va?" I wasn't privy to a lot of the concerns that were discussed in the courtyard. That may have been just as well. Discussing my worries with other worried parents, in the absence of hope, probably would have depressed me, and I was already anxious. Doctor Erika had convinced Ian and me of the worth of her approach, and we were committed to continuing with the supplements and the energy medicine.

Doctor Erika's positive attitude helped lift our sagging spirits during this time. She gave us tools that we could use to increase our resiliency. We all encounter problems in life; it's our ability to handle them that determines whether or not we experience a situation as stressful. When you get knocked down, you get up again. You keep searching until you find the right answer or remedy.

Still, I was afraid of being wrong about Chris, both medically and socially, and Doctor Tissot's pessimistic attitude did nothing to alleviate my fears.

Worn down by the pressures exerted by "professionals," I agreed to Doctor Tissot's suggestion to raise the Leponex slightly. Doctor Erika would have to retest Chris at the higher levels of medication and adjust his supplements accordingly. Raising the medication was not the most desirable option, but it was the path of least resistance.

Ian and I were experiencing a paradigm shift. The view of health and mental health espoused by practitioners of energy medicine was incompatible with the one embraced by the HOPE program, and we received conflicting advice. If we weren't able to integrate the two approaches, we would need to choose one direction or the other.

The clash of paradigms was sucking the energy out of all of us.

Chapter 20

✷ The Never-Ending Battle

IN SEPTEMBER OF 2005, the National Institute of Mental Health (NIMH) announced the results of the CATIE[1] study, which showed that four of the newer antipsychotic medications[2] offered "no substantial advantage" over perphenazine, an older, lower-cost neuroleptic.[3] (This result was unexpected, as the conventional wisdom held that the newer antipsychotic drugs were better than the older ones.[4])

I wasn't impressed by any of the drugs my son had been given, and the more I learned about the mind–body connection, the more convinced I became that a holistic approach to treatment would benefit Chris far more than any prescription drug that researchers could offer.

Actress Margo Kidder tells an amusing story about how she discovered alternatives to psychiatric drugs.[5] After being unsuccessfully treated for years for bipolar disorder, Kidder researched the ingredients in the drugs she was taking and then went to the health food store and bought the natural equivalent. She thought she deserved the Nobel Prize for her insight but realized she would have to share it when she met a woman in the store buying the same products for the same reason!

Kidder was able to figure this out for herself, but people like Chris, who, for one reason or another, are not in a position to help themselves, need an advocate—someone who is willing and able to do the research, ask the questions, and seek out the people and products that will allow them to get back on track.

In the last quarter of 2005, Doctor Tissot lowered Chris's Abilify from 15 mg to 10 mg. At first, I considered the decrease a sign that the staff at HOPE must also have observed the small improvements in Chris's functioning that Ian and I saw. Chris was regularly attending the political science class at Webster, and in tandem with Ian, he had volunteered to usher at our church one Sunday morning. He greeted people as they entered the church, handed out programs for the service, and passed the collection plate at the appropriate time without any signs of undue stress.

I was, therefore, puzzled when Chris came home from the program one day and told me that his Abilify was going back up to 15 mg. I contacted Doctor Tissot, who told me the confusion was caused by a miscommunication between him and his assistant, Doctor Hublot. Doctor Tissot planned to progressively lower the Abilify while simultaneously raising the Leponex from 25 mg to a dosage of between 100 and 150 mg. Chris's medications were being rearranged, not lowered.

I had my issues with Doctor Tissot, but Ian suspected that Doctor Hublot was overriding our requests to lower the medication. Ian disliked Doctor Hublot because he never acknowledged our presence at the family circle, not even a handshake. It wasn't just us. I noticed that he avoided eye contact with other parents and patients. He kept his head down and said little, behaving more like a patient in the program than a member of the staff.

Chris had been taking 50 mg of Leponex for a couple of weeks when I noticed he was experiencing urinary incontinence. (He was also eating constantly, and his weight was higher than ever.) The possibility that he might wet his pants during a class was very real, and the additional weight, as well as being harmful to his health, would attract negative attention. I was concerned that Doctor Tissot's prediction that Chris would be laughed at by other students might become a reality.

Doctor Tissot was about to raise the Leponex dosage to 75 mg. Concerned that even 50 mg might be too high, especially in view of the supplements Chris was taking, I questioned the increase at our monthly meeting.

Doctor Tissot insisted that a dosage of between 75 mg and 100 mg of Leponex was "clearly necessary" to keep Chris's symptoms in check. He agreed that the incontinence was a problem.

"Thanks very much for bringing this to my attention, Madame Forbes. I'll ask Doctor Hublot to schedule Chris for urine and blood tests as well as an EEG. And I'd like to ask Doctor Rx, who, as you know, is a specialist in the pharmacology of psychosis, to come to a future meeting to discuss the results of the EEG."

Chris said very little during the meeting, despite direct appeals for his input about how he was faring in regard to the medication. We all agreed the Leponex would be raised to 75 mg, but after the meeting I had second thoughts. I asked Chris to hold off on filling the prescription until I could find out more from Doctor Tissot about the reasons he was raising the dosage. In our brief conversation, Doctor Tissot said he wanted input from Chris about his dosages. He told me he would meet with Chris the next day and get back to me.

I was vexed. Despite my encouragement, Chris had done no research to learn about the medications he was taking. His ambivalence concerned me, but it was even more of a problem for him. He disliked taking sides and would agree to do whatever someone wanted him to do in order to avoid an argument. Alone with Doctor Tissot, the chances were good that he would allow the meds to be raised. Chris was the person swallowing the pills—so his opinion was clearly important—but he was not aware of the serious side effects and risks presented with long-term use, except for what he learned from me.

If Chris were a child, no doctor would have suggested that he could or should be expected to understand the implications of different treatment alternatives. But, at twenty-one, he was an adult, and Mommy and Daddy weren't supposed to be making decisions for him.

I needn't have worried so much about the outcome of Chris's meeting with Doctor Tissot. In the end, perhaps based on his conversation with Chris, Doctor Tissot kept the Leponex at 50 mg. "Chris seemed to be functioning okay at that level," he wrote in an e-mail.

The urinary problem cleared up on its own. I have no idea why. Maybe Chris used EFT to focus his mind upon healing the underlying cause.

By now, even Ian was losing patience with the HOPE program. Neither of us saw the need for Chris to have an electroencephalogram, and we certainly didn't care to discuss the results in the presence of Doctor Rx, who, I was convinced, was being brought in to intimidate us. (There were already too many medical professionals meddling in our lives. Chris was required to take a blood test every two weeks in order to monitor the Leponex—a medication that caused side effects but hadn't eliminated symptoms.)

The next time we met with Doctor Tissot, Ian and I politely told him that we didn't think meeting with Doctor Rx would be necessary, and we refused to consent to the EEG. We were not happy with Chris's progress, we said, and we wanted all of his medications progressively lowered—to zero. The weight gain in itself was alarming.

I was sick of how complicated everything was, and I was getting seriously bored. Drug therapy, in particular, is boring. (Not surprisingly, supplements were becoming a close second. At this point in Chris's treatment, most of the focus was on getting the correct dosages and ensuring he had all the products he needed.)

Despite everyone's best efforts, no one had yet gotten to the root of Chris's problems. My search for effective solutions continued. Soon, I would discover a completely different way of looking at the origins of schizophrenia.

This new approach, which incorporated shamanistic beliefs and practices, would help me better understand the dynamic interaction of mind, body, and spirit.

I was about to learn what *holistic* really means.

Chapter 21

❋ The Levels of Healing

TOWARD THE END OF 2005, I learned that Doctor Tissot was
planning to prescribe amisulpride (Solian)[1] in addition to the 50 mg
of clozapine (Leponex) that Chris was taking. I had thought that
the Abilify was being phased out in favor of Leponex—and only
Leponex. Chris's doctors had tried Risperdal, Leponex, and Abilify.
How many more drugs were they going to prescribe?

"Madame Forbes," said Doctor Tissot at our hastily arranged
meeting to discuss this latest development, "the literature shows that,
in cases of schizophrenia, two neuroleptic drugs used simultaneously
in low doses work best. That is what we go on in the program."

"Doctor Tissot," I protested, "I don't care what the literature says.
I don't see any improvement in Chris on these drugs, and certainly
not enough to justify what I *am* seeing, which is weight gain and
general mental and physical slowness. Wouldn't it make more sense
to try a new drug singly so its effects could be determined without
confounding variables? Isn't one drug less detrimental than two?"

Ian's and my goal, which was not embraced by Doctor Tissot, was
for Chris to be back at university and, at some point, to be gainfully
employed. I was fighting a lone uphill battle against the HOPE

program in general and against Doctor Tissot in particular. My son was unwilling to take a stand, and my husband wanted me to stop being so fixated on the drugs. "Let's just give this a chance," said Ian.

I was outnumbered. Solian was substituted for Abilify. Chris remained on two major tranquilizers.

Despite my objections to the medications, managing Chris's intake of two prescriptions was far simpler than managing his supplement regimen. He was taking numerous supplements, in various forms. (Doctor Erika had warned me at the start that keeping up with so many products could be onerous, but I never imagined just how onerous it would be.)

I put the pills and capsules into a pill organizer and made sure that Chris took them as prescribed. Some of the products were in liquid form and needed to be mixed with water and drunk over the course of the day; those I mixed at the start of each day.

Doctor Erika monitored Chris's response to the medication adjustments and to the supplements using muscle testing. His needs sometimes changed suddenly; he would take a product for a week or two and then his body would no longer need it, so that product was dropped and a different one was ordered. Our kitchen was overrun with boxes of partially used or still unopened supplements.

While I believed in the efficacy of Doctor Erika's approach, and I continued to see some improvement in my son's ability to concentrate and in his energy level, keeping track of what Chris needed to take and when was way too complex for my liking.

The expense was also mounting. Our health insurance plan didn't cover vitamin supplements. We were willing to do whatever we could for Chris, and, fortunately, we had the resources to follow Doctor Erika's recommendations, but I often wondered how other people handled the cost.

In addition to taking care of Chris, I needed to take better care of myself and learn healthy ways to cope with stress. I'd gained thirteen pounds while taking the Paxil, and I hadn't been able to shed the extra weight through dieting. I felt sluggish, and I ached all over from lack of exercise. My right shoulder, which had been causing me pain for years, was particularly sore, and it cracked whenever I rotated it.

A coworker practiced Reiki, a form of hands-on healing that originated in Japan, and I told her I was interested in seeing what she could do for my shoulder. Cécilia stopped by my office during her lunch hour and held my shoulder for about thirty minutes. The intense heat coming from her hands amazed me.

Cécilia listened with evident interest when I talked about Chris's problems. She was knowledgeable about many alternative healing techniques and suggested I read up on Bert Hellinger's Family Constellation work. I brushed off the suggestion as being too far out of my comfort zone and belief system.

"Don't be too quick to judge," Cécilia said. "Stay open to healing possibilities. You don't know when or where they might happen."

Cécilia promised to send me an article (in French) about a much-persecuted German doctor named Ryke Geerd Hamer.

"His story perfectly illustrates the truth of the old saying, 'in every crisis there is opportunity.' You'll understand when you read the article."

Soon after Cécilia left my office, my shoulder pain was gone. When she later sent me the article about Doctor Hamer, I read it with interest.

Ryke Geerd Hamer, MD is famous (and infamous) in Europe for his "Iron Rules of Cancer" theory and the astonishing success rate he claims with terminal cancer patients. His approach (called German New Medicine) grew out of a tragic event that occurred in 1978 when Hamer and his physician wife maintained clinical practices in Rome. Seventeen-year-old Dirk, the second of their four children, was sleeping on a boat anchored off Corsica when a gun was fired from a nearby yacht. Dirk was struck by a stray bullet and lingered in a coma for four months before dying in his father's arms. When Doctor Hamer developed testicular cancer several years later, he was convinced that the shock of Dirk's death played a role in its development.[2]

Hamer subsequently decided to focus on cancer research, hypothesizing that cancer and other diseases originate from an unexpected trauma or shock, which causes a lesion in the brain.

Most cancers and cancer-equivalent ailments, according to Doctor Hamer, begin with "Dirk Hamer Syndrome"—a severe, acute, and unexpected shock that creates a "biological conflict" and occurs simultaneously in the psyche, the brain, and an organ.[3] The shock that registers in the brain can be identified as concentric circles (Hamer Herds) using computed tomography (CT). The nature of the biological conflict determines the location of the Hamer Herds and the organ in the body on which the cancer (or "cancer-equivalent disease") will be found.[4]

In the case of schizophrenia, Hamer has found two concentric circles, which register as a result of two active biological conflicts.[5] Hamer believes that this phenomenon results when the individual sees no way of resolving a conflict.[6]

After reading about Hamer's theory, I started to think about the possible role of trauma as a causal factor in the development of both schizophrenia and cancer. I had heard people comment from time to time that Chris must have suffered a shock at some point. "Poor boy," said a homeopathic consultant I once met with briefly, "he must have suffered quite a shock." I had no idea what she was talking about.

The shock theory as the basis of schizophrenia is not new in psychiatric circles. Loren Mosher, MD, the first head of the National Institute of Mental Health's Center for Studies of Schizophrenia[7] described psychosis as an understandable coping mechanism, similar to shell shock but distinguished by an important difference: the shell-shock victim's trauma is readily identifiable. ("It's right there, easy to see."[8]) In contrast, the trauma that schizophrenics have experienced "is more often cumulative, rather than a single event."[9] Usually, Mosher says, there is also a trigger event (e.g., a romantic rejection, the death of a parent, recreational drug use).[10]

I had dismissed that line of thinking early on because I was not aware of any severe shocks or trauma that Chris had suffered, and I knew he wasn't using street drugs. After reading Doctor Hamer's research, I was willing to revisit the issue, though I still couldn't identify a triggering event in Chris's life.

I recalled his disappointment over Ophelia. Could unrequited love produce such a terrifying outcome as schizophrenia? And if that rejection had been the trigger, would Chris have trouble healing because of the chronic stress and feelings of hopelessness that accompany the diagnosis once it's delivered? Was the diagnosis of schizophrenia an obstacle to full recovery?

I concluded that I had been an idiot for listening to the staff at CAMH when they advised me not to read about the illness. Now I was prepared to act on almost any theory or idea that made some sort of intuitive sense.

While browsing online one day, I came across some interesting information that made me think magnetic therapy might be useful for Chris. The earth has lost much of its magnetism over the past several thousand years, I learned. Scientists believe that this decline is a sign of pole reversal, a switch in magnetic north and south poles. Some researchers postulate that the dramatic change in magnetic energy on earth is a causal factor in insomnia, headaches, joint stiffness, and other chronic conditions.[11] Because the subatomic building blocks of our cellular structure emit positive and negative electrical energies, imbalances in the earth's magnetic field affect our health.

In an article published in the official journal of the Schizophrenia International Research Society (SIRS), Ronald W. Kay noted that, in the Northern Hemisphere, a significant number of individuals with a diagnosis of schizophrenia had been born in winter or spring.[12] (Chris was born in January.) Kay hypothesized that seasonal variations in the geomagnetic field of the earth during gestation could have an effect on the rate at which schizophrenia later develops.

I decided to order a magnetic mattress for Chris, without clearing it with Doctor Erika or Doctor Tissot. Magnetism is a natural phenomenon, and I reasoned that even if the mattress did not result in better sleep and less anxiety (as my research suggested it might), using it would, in all likelihood, do Chris no harm. While I had the highest respect for Doctor Erika, Chris and I couldn't wait years for her to go to a conference, learn about the value of magnetism, and then recommend it to her patients.[13] I didn't need a prescription—or a doctor's approval—to buy a mattress, so I didn't see any point in mentioning it to Doctor Tissot. His views about nutritional supplements were clear enough; I had no expectation that he would be the least bit interested in or impressed by the benefits of magnetic therapy, and I didn't need to give him one more reason to label me a troublemaker—or a kook!

Within a few days of sleeping on the mattress, Chris seemed more relaxed, and he commented that he was well rested. (Our houseguests occasionally borrowed Chris's bed and always reported a fabulous sleep on that mattress.)

Any change that resulted in a net improvement, no matter how small, was good news to me. The accumulation of small gains that I was seeing in Chris from the supplements, the EFT, and the magnetic mattress gave me hope. But it often seemed that I was the only person actually noticing. I usually had to point these small improvements out to Ian, who would then tend to agree with my observations. Doctor Tissot was a lost cause. If he didn't notice an improvement, then, clinically, there was no improvement.

For Christmas that year, Ian bought me a book called *The Natural Medicine Guide to Schizophrenia*.[14] The author, Stephanie Marohn, seemed to have overcome some serious health issues of her own and had written a series of books on the natural treatment of mental health conditions such as autism, depression, and bipolar disorder. The *Natural Medicine Guide* introduced me to some astounding healing practices, which were presented in the context of levels of healing, a model developed by Dietrich Klinghardt, MD, PhD, a physician who maintains practices in the United States and in Europe.

Klinghardt identified five levels of healing that form a healing pyramid.[15] An unresolved issue at a higher level can prevent the healing of a disturbance at a lower level. (For example, a problem within a family system (level 4) can impact levels 1 to 3, the physical, electromagnetic, and mental bodies.) Resolution of the issue at the highest level can rapidly change the lower levels, which may correct without further intervention.)

The first level of the healing pyramid (the base) is the physical. Diagnostic methods include physical examinations and laboratory tests. Healing interventions may involve the use of drugs, surgery, vitamin supplements, herbs, nutrition, and so on.

Next is the electromagnetic level, which governs modulation of the electrical and magnetic currents within the body and the body's energy field (the electromagnetic field that is produced by the body and surrounds it like an aura). Therapeutic interventions include acupuncture, Ayurvedic medicine, and techniques that affect the body's electromagnetic system. Level 3, the mental level, includes beliefs, thoughts, and attitudes; this is the traditional realm of psychology. Interventions at this level work with the conscious and subconscious aspects of the mind. Effective therapies include classical homeopathy and psychotherapy.

Level 4 is the intuitive level—the realm of dreams, trance, meditative states, out-of-body experiences, and the collective unconscious. According to Doctor Klinghardt, shamanic healing operates at this level (as does Family Constellation work, which I had dismissed when Cécilia suggested it to me several weeks earlier).

Level 5, the peak of the healing pyramid, is the spiritual level, the realm in which one develops a relationship with a higher power (call it God, if you will). Healing at this level is up to the individual; it's beyond the scope of doctors and medical interventions. (Level 4, then, would be the highest level I could explore with Chris.)

Doctor Klinghardt believes that schizophrenia is usually caused by a disturbance on either level 1 (physical) or level 4 (intuitive), with level 4 being more common.[16]

If level 4 held the key to Chris's recovery, the HOPE program was never going to rise to the challenge. Its emphasis on managing symptoms with drugs was strictly Level 1, and though some attention was paid to psychosocial remediation (through exercise and group activities), the subtler realms that are characteristic of Level 4 (and difficult to quantify in scientific terms) were beyond the scope of most conventional medical practices.

I would have to venture outside mainstream medicine to find practitioners who knew how to navigate this territory.

Chapter 22

Beyond the Mainstream ✳

BORED WITH DOLING OUT medications and supplements—
and frustrated that I wasn't seeing dramatic improvement in Chris—I
took a closer look at some of the psychiatrists who had challenged
mainstream views about schizophrenia and other mental illnesses in
the 1960s and 1970s.

Thomas Szasz, MD, a psychiatrist and academic, noted that
among scientists and physicians the classic definition of disease refers
to bodily (organic) abnormalities.[1] The brain is an organ and can be
diseased; the mind, however, is not an organ and can only be "ill" in
a metaphorical sense (as in a sick mind, an ill society, or a cancerous
idea). According to Szasz, psychiatrists treat "problems in living," not
organic illnesses.[2] As such, mental illness can be seen as a coping
strategy, maybe even a choice.

Loren Mosher, MD, a contemporary of Szasz and R.D. Laing,
MD (a charismatic psychiatrist who founded an experimental treatment community in London), was open-minded about the cause—and
treatment—of schizophrenia. Unconvinced that schizophrenia is an
organic disease, Mosher obtained a grant to compare the outcomes of
different treatment modalities for individuals who were experiencing

their first psychotic episodes. Some of the funds from the grant were used to start Soteria, a residential community center for people aged 18 to 30 who had recently been diagnosed with schizophrenia.[3]

Doctor Mosher described his treatment approach as "being with," "standing by attentively," "trying to put your feet into the other person's shoes," and "being an LSD trip guide."[4] The Soteria program was found to be as successful as anti-psychotic drug treatment in reducing psychotic symptoms in six weeks.[5] (The Soteria staff refrained, when possible, from administering neuroleptic drugs or major tranquilizers during the first six weeks an individual was in residence; if no improvement was noted after six weeks, a trial drug treatment might be initiated.[6])

Like many other mental health professionals of the time, Mosher put the blame for schizophrenia on the parents:

> There are two aspects of family life that have been consistently highly associated with what's called schizophrenia. One has been dubbed 'communication deviance.' It's simple. Just means that when you sit with these parents, you can't figure out what the hell it is they're talking about. They can't focus on things. You can't visualize what they say. They go off on tangents. They are loose in the way that they think.[7]

I was troubled by Mosher's facile assumptions about individuals and families he didn't really know. (I had reservations in this regard about Laing, too.) Mosher's comments reflected the views of researchers and clinicians, who, during that era, often singled out poor parenting as one of the main causes of mental illness. (One study looked at how the mothers of schizophrenics performed on a Rorschach test. Results showed a mixture of disordered thoughts and a distorted view of reality,[8] giving the researchers the impression that the women suffered from "diluted schizophrenia."[9])

Social worker Jacqui Schiff, for example, blamed the failure of parents to send the right messages to their children for the subsequent development of schizophrenia. In her book, *All My Children*, published in 1970, Schiff was particularly harsh on mothers. She and her husband had taken a number of schizophrenic young people into their household in order to "reparent" them. Despite my misgivings about some of her methods (e.g., diapering young adults and feeding them milk from baby bottles)—as well as her self-righteous attitude—Schiff's book does provide a rare glimpse into round-the-clock support in a home setting with minimal use of drugs.

The idea that schizophrenia could be considered an altered state (rather than a medical condition) intrigued me, but, without practical advice (and support) to help families cope with the demands of caring for a loved one, these ideas seemed more theoretical than practical. Where were the self-help books outlining the steps parents could take to facilitate recovery? If these "experts" were so persuaded that the family environment was a major factor in the development of schizophrenia, why didn't they teach parents the communication skills needed to create a healing environment? Their message, instead, served to underscore the importance of psychiatrists and other professionals as essential players in the treatment of dysfunction, leaving parents and families dependent upon outsiders for help and advice.

I recognized that these unconventional professionals were, like their more mainstream counterparts, influenced by the widely held beliefs of their time, and I decided I would not reject outright everything they had to say just because they seemed out of line on the parenting issue. I was open to the possibility that I was in some way responsible for Chris's problems. If I needed to change so that he could recover, then I would change. Seeing Chris get well was more important than protecting my ego.

Not all parents were willing to consider the possibility that the home environment could have been a factor in the development of their child's mental illness, however; many reacted to the suggestion as "parent-blaming," and some banded together in the late 1970s to form NAMI. (NAMI emphasizes the role of the brain, not the role of the family, in the development (and treatment) of mental illness.) In the decades that it has been in existence, NAMI has become an influential lobbying group.

And what is the role of the individual in all of these approaches? I wondered. Must patients remain passive recipients while others decide their fate?

My confidence that Chris could recover—without drugs and outside of an institutional setting—grew stronger as I searched outside the narrow confines of mainstream understanding.

With renewed optimism, I turned my attention to level 4, the realm of the symbolic, the mythic, the shamanic.

Chapter 23

The World Is a Stage ✳

IN THE WINTER MONTHS of 2006, Chris became a bit more
talkative. He started volunteering his thoughts and ideas. His speech
was less broken up by gaps while he thought things through. He
spoke with enthusiasm about the class he was auditing at Webster. I
noticed that he was turning lights on when he entered a room. Before,
he often sat in the dark.

I (perhaps wrongly) attributed these changes more to his daily practice of Emotional Freedom Technique and to the magnetic mattress he
had recently started sleeping on than to the effects of Doctor Erika's
supplements, which Chris had now been taking for over six months.
So many different interventions had been tried that determining the
specific effects of each one was impossible; my husband and I tended to
attribute new improvements to whatever had been recently introduced.

Chris had been participating in the highly touted HOPE program
for more than a year and a half; he'd been taking antipsychotic drugs
for two years. If this treatment approach was going to be effective for
him, I thought, it should have produced better results by now.

The tranquilizers kept him sluggish and overweight, and he
had trouble getting up in the morning. He continued to make

those popping noises and whistling sounds, which, as far as I could remember, he had been doing since beginning the clozapine (Leponex). He was taking 50 mg of clozapine and 200 mg of amisulpride (Solian) daily and was tired a lot of the time. He asked to have the Solian lowered, which, in itself, was a step forward. Predictably, however, Doctor Tissot had a different view, and the dosage stayed the same.

One day in mid-March, I opened an e-mail from Doctor Erika. Despite the fact that we had recently signed a renewed consent form to allow her to continue treating Chris, she was feeling uneasy about our long-distance relationship. One of her patients had ended up back in hospital while she was on vacation, and she was doubting her ability to treat patients that she couldn't see on a regular basis. Her e-mail was an unexpected setback. We were counting on her guidance to safely get Chris off the meds.

I didn't respond for a couple of days so that I could buck up my spirits. I reassured her as much as I could; we were here to stay no matter what, I told her, and we depended on her for moral support as well as treatment advice.

Being in the position of having to help a psychiatrist "get over it" felt odd, but, thankfully, she did, and we resumed where we'd left off.

Ian and I dutifully attended monthly meetings with Doctor Tissot. To our disappointment, Chris's clinical presentation at these meetings continued to be poor. His discomfort was no doubt partly due to the ongoing tension between Ian and me over the meds. Though we were determined to present a unified front, disagreement over the drugs created frustration and conflict in our marital relationship. My exasperation sometimes spilled over onto Chris.

"Chris, can't you just fake being normal for once?" I berated him after a meeting with Doctor Tissot. "Doctor Tissot holds the keys to the insane asylum. You need his blessing or he will never agree to lower the meds."

Unfortunately, Chris did not seem able to fake his way out of whatever it was that was keeping him labeled "hopeless" by the staff at the HOPE program.

Doctor Tissot told us at our next meeting that the staff had been instructed to treat Chris gently. "We think that Chris is intelligent, but we don't know what the problem is, why he isn't improving," he told us.

Chris had great difficulty using scissors to cut paper during art class, we learned.

"But, you know," said Doctor Tissot, smiling at Chris, "we are amazed that he is very good in acting class."

I realized then that I no longer cared about Doctor Tissot's clinical impressions. *Maybe the clinic is the problem*, I thought.

True, it didn't look good not to be able to cut paper at his age, but then why was Chris able to do these things—and more—at home? He was quite good at fixing things around the apartment. And what kind of "art therapy" was this anyway? Chris probably felt like he was in kindergarten, cutting paper with scissors. Maybe he felt pressured to perform and disliked being judged and evaluated. Who wants to be compared to an apple when you are an orange, or maybe even a grape? I was beginning to think that an institution was possibly the last place anyone would get well.

Before our meeting ended, Doctor Tissot shared his observation that Chris "came alive" during acting class. "What would you think of doing some play acting at home?" he asked.

Chris immediately brightened.

"Good! Then may I suggest that you and your family start with *Waiting for Godot*? The play reminds me of you."

Doctor Tissot was normally not given to making suggestions about ways that we, the parents, could be involved, leaving us with the impression that he believed the HOPE staff knew what was best for our son and wished we would just let them get on with it. The idea of a play was brilliant.

Thereafter, for a brief period, we enlivened our evenings (which had, of late, been spent watching sitcoms and self-medicating with a bottle of wine) by playacting. Following Doctor Tissot's advice, we started with *Waiting for Godot*. Ian assigned our roles: Taylor was Pozzo; Chris was Vladimir. Ian read the part of Estragon; I narrated and took the smaller parts.

Chris stepped outside of himself and inhabited his character. Doctor Tissot was right. He has a flair for the dramatic.

After several evenings, we switched to poetry readings. In a clear and confident voice, and with evident feeling, Chris recited Robert Frost's "Fire and Ice" from memory:

> Some say the world will end in fire,
> Some say in ice.
> From what I've tasted of desire
> I hold with those who favor fire.
> But if it had to perish twice,
> I think I know enough of hate
> To know that for destruction ice
> Is also great
> And would suffice.

O schizophrenia! Fire/ice, love/hate. Ambivalence and death with a dollop of guilt thrown in.

Doctor Tissot had, on more than a few occasions when we met with him, hinted that Chris was making a fool of him and everybody else at HOPE, as he was not getting well. Did Doctor Tissot suspect that Chris was acting? I had wondered the same thing at times.

The reality of Chris's debilitated physical and mental state was difficult to reconcile with the idea that he could be *acting* psychotic, but R. D. Laing evidently thought that much of the behavior that results in a diagnosis of "schizophrenia" is just that: *playing at* madness.[1]

Why might my son want to "act crazy"? To avoid accountability for his own thoughts and intentions.

If Chris was acting mad or ill to avoid responsibility, then his avoidance behavior would come as a welcome relief. Shirking responsibility, while still problematic, would be a far simpler problem to address than a diagnosis of schizophrenia.

Through Chris, our whole family had been drawn into the theater
of the absurd as a means of coping with the ongoing drama that Life
with Chris created. We'd been living out a Greek tragedy, but if we
could comprehend Chris's way of communicating—and if he could
comprehend ours—he might choose to "act normal," something most
of us attempt to do each day, with varying degrees of success.

Our story was not yet at an end, but I'd reached several conclu-
sions about Chris's condition:

> **Message Number 1** (from Doctor Hoffer): Nobody
> who relies on drugs alone will ever get well.

> **Message Number 2** (from Doctor Klinghardt): If
> schizophrenia isn't resolved by therapies aimed at the
> first (physical) level, look to the fourth (intuitive) level.

> **Message Number 3** (from Doctor Tissot and R.D.
> Laing): The play's the thing.

I was ready to move beyond Act Two, in which the medications
took center stage.

Chapter 24

❈ *Expressing Emotion*

IAN AND I had separate business trips scheduled at the end of April (2006). Alex was finishing his first year at Purdue University in Indiana, and Taylor planned to be away over spring break with friends from high school. Chris would be alone for the first time in the two years since he'd returned from Toronto.

I offered to find someone to stay with him, but he said he'd be fine. While the situation was less than ideal, he assured us that he could get himself to the HOPE program each day, take his medications, and prepare his own meals.

I packaged his daily medications and supplements in advance, laid in a supply of food, and harped on the necessity of keeping in contact with Ian and me every day by e-mail or by phone. We told some of our close friends that he would be home alone, and we gave Chris their phone numbers in case he needed to call. (We didn't tell Doctor Tissot; he would have questioned our actions and caused us to doubt the wisdom of our choices.) Hoping for the best, we left Chris to fend for himself.

The first two days passed without incident. Chris sent e-mails letting us know that he was "fine" and we needn't worry. On the third day,

I got a couple of lines signed "Loner," an indication that he was going downhill fast. Then, not a word. From a distance, there wasn't much Ian or I could do. We knew that Chris was conscientious and would do what he had to do to take care of himself. We hoped so, anyway.

At the end of the week, I arrived back at our apartment in the late afternoon and discovered that the door was not just locked, but chained from the inside. I rang the bell. The door opened a crack. From somewhere in the darkness beyond, an extraterrestrial creature waved a mutant eyeball in my direction.

I spoke in a calm voice so that I wouldn't alarm him. "Can you let me in, please?"

Chris slowly shut the door and removed the chain. The door creaked open and I rushed in (a little too enthusiastically, perhaps) to greet my traumatized son. He backed away from me. The shades were drawn, and the room was completely dark. Chris peered at me from a safe distance, behaving as if he'd never seen a human before.

"How have you been, Chris?" I asked as I approached him.

"How have I beeehhhnnn?" he responded, in a high, quavering voice.

I grasped his shoulders with both hands.

Chris peered at me again, his face close to mine, examining my head in relation to the rest of my body. "Mother, you have a very small head," he announced.

Instantly, I knew: He was hallucinating. I suspected he had spent the week in near darkness; he'd probably also skipped his meds. No one from the HOPE program had contacted Ian or me, so I'd assumed Chris had been attending as usual.

Seeing him in this state reminded me how much he needed people around him to stem the loneliness and to keep him from sliding into psychosis. It would be years before I would leave him alone again for longer than a day.

I vowed not to divulge the incident to Doctor Tissot, who would likely respond with more meds.

In a few days, Chris was more or less back to the state he'd been in before Ian, Taylor, and I all left. (Not surprisingly, he recovered faster at home than he did at the program.) Ian and I relaxed a bit in the knowledge that he wouldn't suffer any long-term harm from occasional setbacks. We were learning to ride out the rough patches.

Doctor Tissot, however, noticed that something was off and called Ian, Chris, and me in for a meeting. Now somewhat wiser parents, Ian and I rehearsed our roles in advance. We were going to be the genial, loving, and slightly clueless parents who hadn't noticed anything unusual about their son's recent behavior, and who were absolutely delighted with his progress up until now. Our acting routine must have worked. For once, Doctor Tissot, didn't even raise the subject of the medication.

My husband and I recognized that we needed to develop better ways of responding to Chris's unpredictable and sometimes frightening behavior. Our home life during this trying period of our lives was increasingly stressful. Ian, Chris, Taylor, and I were living on top of each other 24/7, and everyone's nerves were shot. (Alex came home twice a year, at Christmas and during the summer.) Because of his special needs, Chris took up most of our time—and space. We often pointed out to him how, "for his own good," he should behave differently, as if he could change by "trying" a little harder.

I took the lead by changing my own behavior. I didn't want to become an impediment to my son's recovery.

In 1962, Brown et al. reported on the results of a study designed to test the hypothesis that a schizophrenic patient would be more likely to deteriorate after hospitalization if he was returning to a home in which one or more family members expressed strong emotion, hostility, or dominating behavior.[1] After following 128 schizophrenic men discharged from London hospitals, the researchers found higher rates of deterioration for men returning to homes in which "high emotional involvement" was shown by relatives.

Families of mentally ill patients don't like to hear that they may be preventing their relatives from getting well (or that poor parenting or sending mixed messages might have contributed to their children's mental, emotional, and behavioral problems)—especially if the implication is that *they* may need to change somehow. Suggestions may be interpreted as accusations, and if they sometimes act hostile and unloving, family members may fear that clinicians will judge them for their failures and imperfections. But parents and other significant figures may be more open to learning new communication skills if they realize that learning new skills can help them improve their relationships and lessen tensions for all concerned. The degree of emotional expression can be seen as a measure of how stressful the current home environment is (rather than a reflection of the dynamics that were at work in the past).

Instead of treating Chris as a "problem to be fixed," I learned to see him as an otherwise interesting, somewhat quirky human being who happened to be going through a very difficult period in his life, and I looked for ways to improve the quality of our interactions.

I instinctively knew that pitying my son would not help him. (Family members may think they are being kind and empathetic when they lower their expectations of what their relative can hope to achieve, but if they view the person as chronically ill and brain-damaged, their attitude will come across as pity, and pity only adds to the person's feelings of inadequacy.)

To help me avoid getting sucked into the pity trap, I steered clear of naysayers, the people who believe that schizophrenia is always chronic and has to be managed by professionals (i.e., with drugs). Many of the better-known names in the field of mental health were among the naysayers. Ignoring them was easy; I just didn't buy their books or listen to their opinions.

I couldn't completely ignore my friends and relatives, though. Most of them accepted the mainstream view—that schizophrenia is caused by a dysfunctional brain. The solution, I found, was to stop discussing Chris with them. For several years, to all intents and purposes, I had two sons, not three. Better to keep quiet, I thought, than feel obliged to give progress reports when progress was not apparent to anyone else.

Another kind of emotional overinvolvement is what I call "cheerleading." Cheerleading is similar to pity, though less destructive when motivated by genuine love and interest. (In my efforts to be a supportive mom, I often complimented Chris's behavior and appearance.)

Positive feedback works—up to a point. I thought I was being supportive if I encouraged Chris every day to improve himself in every way. In hindsight, I think I should have exercised more restraint. My praise may have sounded artificial and insincere to him, bordering on pity, and my overinvolvement sometimes slid into "constructive criticism." Just because Chris wasn't ready to take on bigger projects, according to my timetable, didn't mean that he would never be ready. I had plenty of opportunities to cultivate patience.

Choosing not to express dissatisfaction became easier when I saw the effect of my behavior on Chris. Criticism isn't just verbal; actions and facial expressions—and diagnoses—convey blame, disappointment, and judgment. Over time, I learned to keep a poker face instead of rolling my eyes or grimacing when confronted with some new and unusual behavior.

My husband and I eventually figured out that our relationship improved when we didn't discuss Chris's problems. Practically speaking, that meant not talking about Chris at all. (Talking about Chris inevitably led to fighting about medications. Ian knew my views; I knew his. Too many words had already passed between us.)

Our new strategy worked—for Ian and me, and for Chris. If Ian and I weren't fighting about Chris and what was best for him, then Chris was not affected by the fallout. He was moving out of our minds, if not out of our apartment.

Staying open to change was essential if I wanted to help my son succeed—whether that meant changing my beliefs or my behavior. My aim was to spare Chris from identifying himself as a mental patient. I intended to continue seeking out noninvasive interventions, which usually meant looking outside the mainstream mental health system.

I was familiar with basic principles of energy medicine (chakras, vibrational frequencies, meridians and the like), and I knew that certain practices and techniques (EFT, yoga, acupuncture, etc.) can help balance and harmonize mind, body, and spirit. Soon I would learn about "the assemblage point" and its importance in maintaining physical and mental well being.

Chapter 25

The Assemblage Point ✳

CHRIS'S SPOOKY BEHAVIOR when left alone for a week prompted me to dig a little deeper into the shamanic view of energy. From the books of Carlos Castaneda[1] and other materials I found online, I learned that the assemblage point is the center of the human energy system and is located in the center of the chest.

Angela Blaen, PhD, notes that as far back as the philosopher Lucretius, the "seat of the intellect and the mind" has been associated with a range of emotions that are felt in the center of the chest.[2] According to Blaen, the position of the assemblage point influences the chakras (as well as the glands and organs each chakra is associated with), the immune system, body posture, and the skin, which is also an organ.[3] Traumatic events, illnesses, accidents, and drug abuse can cause the assemblage point to move out of its proper position.[4] Doctor Blaen has found that people with schizophrenia and bipolar conditions often have two or more shadows or splits.[5] Until the assemblage point is restored to its natural condition, problems are likely to persist.

In Castaneda's tales, the Yaqui medicine man don Juan often used hallucinogenic plants to move the assemblage point, but don Juan also shifted someone's awareness by delivering a sudden thump to the back, a move he called "the nagual's blow"[6] and others refer to as "the shaman's blow."[7]

When I learned that Doctor Blaen used electronic gem therapy and crystals (as well as the shaman's blow) to address misaligned and split assemblage points, I contacted her at her center in Devon, England and booked two appointments for Chris.[8]

I didn't expect these two sessions to solve all of Chris's problems, but I was ready to explore new territory, literally and figuratively. However, I also wondered what I was getting myself into. Who was this Angela Blaen and what did I know about her, apart from her interest in lapidaries and Celtic lore? (The Devon area is known as a center of Celtic culture and Arthurian legends.) Blaen's unconventional practices and offbeat interests made her seem like a rather eccentric character. Was I was willing to entrust my welfare and that of my son to a stranger who might perform some kind of ritual spell-casting? The answer was yes, I would. ("In for a penny, in for a pound," as the British say.)

The day before Chris's appointment, Chris and I flew to Bristol and took the express bus from the airport to the train station. We boarded a train to Exeter and spent the night at a hotel. In the morning, we got an early train to Crediton and had lunch at the tearoom in the station. I bought a book about faeries and West Country lore in the gift shop.

Angela Blaen had arranged for her son, Tom, to meet us at the station at 1:00 p.m., and he arrived on schedule, dressed in black. A doctoral student at Exeter University, Tom was not much older than Chris. The three of us climbed into his tiny car, and we were off!

Hurtling around and through the hedgerows, I felt like Alice going down the rabbit hole. Occasionally, Tom had to pull over to the side of the narrow road, pausing briefly to let another car pass. After about twenty minutes, we landed in front of an old farmhouse. As I got out of the car, I heard a rooster crowing in the distance. Huge hens patrolled the front garden like army sentinels.

A smiling, middle-aged woman with long black hair greeted us from the doorway of a garden shed. She wore a billowing blouse and a colorful skirt. As I got closer, I was immediately captivated by the huge moonstone pendant that hung from a gold chain around her neck.

"Doctor Blaen, I presume?"

"Welcome to our little corner of the world," she said. "Did Tom tell you that the name of our hamlet, Neopardy, is an ancient reference to the turnips that used to grow in the surrounding fields?"

This is going to be fun! I thought as Chris, Tom, and I followed Doctor Blaen into the shed, which had been converted into a treatment room.

The room provided ample space for a small desk and chair, an examining table, electronic equipment, a pile of blankets, and several large wands made of quartz crystal. After some pleasant chitchat about our trip and our reasons for being there, Doctor Blaen took a brief medical history. The assemblage point procedure presented no risks from a medical standpoint, she told Chris and me, but people with a high-left assemblage point sometimes became violent during a session.

"As a precaution," Doctor Blaen said, "I recommend that an assistant be in the room; that's why Tom is here. Also, I find that when two people of the opposite sex work together, balancing the healing energies is easier."

She asked Chris to stand and face her and then gently passed her hand over his chest. When she came to a certain spot, Chris swayed slightly as if thrown off-balance.

Chris's assemblage point had split into three; two spots were equidistant from the central chest position, to the high left and high right. Two similar points were found on Chris's back.

"These are the typical split assemblage point locations indicating schizophrenia," Doctor Blaen said. Displaced centers are often found in patients who have experienced trauma early in life, she told us.

The third spot, on Chris's back, indicated that he speaks more than one language. "That makes sense, Chris, as you live in Switzerland," Doctor Blaen said.

She described the two methods she uses to shift the assemblage point back into position.

"You have a choice, Chris. We can either use crystal wands and a sharp blow to the shoulder blade, or we can use electronic gem therapy." She gestured to an apparatus next to the exam table.

Chris pointed to the gem therapy equipment.

Doctor Blaen nodded with understanding. "A sharp blow doesn't sound very appealing, does it? It's actually not that bad, and it's over quickly, but I imagine you've been poked and prodded enough by now."

Before treating him, Doctor Blaen asked Chris to sign a consent form. Next, she placed two transducers directly in contact with Chris's clothing (at the front and back central positions, where his assemblage point should be) and turned them on.

"These transducers contain gemstone cups with both diamond and carnelian stones," Doctor Blaen explained. "Diamond is used because it's the strongest of the gems, in energy terms. Carnelian promotes balance and energizes the spleen, a beneficial treatment for depression. It's also used for people whose assemblage point is positioned too low. It raises their energy levels."

Over the next twenty minutes, the transducers would pulse vibrational energy through the gemstones, creating a vortex that would draw the split assemblage points back into their proper position and bind them together.

As Chris settled in for his treatment, I inquired about the theory behind the shifts and splits that could affect the assemblage point.

"The position of the assemblage point during childhood is very important," Doctor Blaen said. "Children with seriously misaligned assemblage points find it difficult to interact with others. Around the age of ten, some assemblage points begin to split. The child may develop an interest in mysticism or begin to experience subtle changes. If there's a trauma or shock in the teen years or thereabouts, the symptoms of schizophrenia may begin to manifest."

And that's when it hit me: Chris's intense interest in the fantasy card game began around the age of ten, the age that the psychiatrist at CAMH had asked about but never explained. Perhaps Chris's assemblage point was breaking up at that time.

I was absolutely fascinated by Doctor Blaen. I learned that many of her clients and graduates of her gem therapy course lived in and around Amsterdam, a city famous for its liberal drug policies—the hallucinogenic connection again.

Doctor Blaen told me about one of her patients, a man in his late fifties who had been an epileptic for most of his life. During a typical day he had many seizures, and each time his assemblage point would be jerked out of its central position and dropped into the stomach area. He needed many treatments before his assemblage point stayed in its proper position. With no change to his medication, he had been free from seizures for two years and was able to drive again.

When Chris's treatment was finished, I asked Doctor Blaen what changes we should expect in the coming weeks.

"Chris may become more emotionally expressive," she said. "You may begin to notice that he walks taller and has a better complexion."

As he walked along the garden path, I noticed that Chris was, indeed, walking taller. His face, which had always been rather pale (though less so with the niacinamide), began to flood with color. I was amazed. Was this merely the power of suggestion or was it the power of the assemblage point shift? Maybe it was both. Something magical had happened in that garden shed.

Chris and I climbed back into the car with Tom, who deposited us at the station just in time to catch the train to Exeter, where we again spent the night. Doctor Blaen had suggested that we not rush back to Geneva, because Chris might be tired after the session.

He wasn't tired, so we walked to a restaurant near our hotel for a late dinner. I kept up my end of the conversation, but Chris, as usual, was quiet. He didn't say much about the treatment, nor could he say if he'd felt anything during or after the treatment.

I knew that something beneficial was happening to him, even if he wasn't yet able to articulate his experience. Any sign of progress, no matter how subtle, was encouraging.

Someday, I believed, Chris would be well enough to make his own choices about treatments and practices that contributed to his health and well-being. I wanted him to know that he had options; he didn't need to agree to a plan someone else proposed if it wasn't right for him. I wanted him to learn how to take initiative, so that in the future he would be free to explore the world on his own terms and *find out* what did and did not work for him, without fear. I wanted to see him embrace life with the recognition that a wrong move—a "failure"—was not the end of the world. I wanted him to develop the confidence to take risks and to learn from mistakes rather than berating himself for slipping up. In short, I wanted him to "find" himself and I wanted him to be independent.

I was willing to help my son find his way; I just didn't want to be the caretaker forever. As long as someone cooked his meals, arranged his treatments, and monitored his every move, Chris would remain dependent.

Despite my impatience and frustration at times, I recognized that these things have their own timing. Healing takes as long as it takes. The time for liberation was still a long way off.

Chapter 26

A Shift in Awareness ✳

BACK IN GENEVA after our trip to see Angela Blaen, I pondered the notion that Chris's assemblage point had started to split when he was ten. Had he shown signs of schizophrenia back then?

I recalled seeing ten-year-old Chris peering out the windows of our home in Ottawa, frightened that he was being chased by "bullies." Did the existential issues he'd been struggling with since he graduated from high school stem from that early experience? Over coffee one morning, I broached the subject with him.

"Chris, I'd like to ask you about something that has been puzzling me. Remember the time you came running home from the park, absolutely terrified? What exactly happened that day?"

Chris flushed slightly; his eyes narrowed. He shook his head and looked down at the table. "Mom, I don't want to say much about it except that I saw a spaceship land in the park, and I saw extraterrestrials get out and they were chasing me!"

Very little about my son surprised me anymore; I wasn't about to get hysterical over this latest revelation. I poured myself another cup of coffee and said, "I see. Well, that must have been exciting. I had never seen you run until then."

When I heard Chris's story, my first thought was that if his hallucinations had been going on for that many years, maybe he'd been ill for too long to get well. On further reflection, I decided to change my thoughts. *So what* if he'd shown signs of schizophrenia when he was ten? Schizophrenia probably doesn't just pop up out of nowhere at seventeen or eighteen. It didn't necessarily mean he couldn't get well, despite what I'd been told by "the experts."

This reframing practice was becoming habitual. My beliefs were subject to modification. If I found a new approach that was in conflict with my current understanding, I was open to learning something new if it would further my son's recovery. I believed everything; I believed nothing.

Thinking of Chris's experience in the park as spiritual, rather than pathological, helped reassure me. After all, his story had a Biblical precedent. In the Book of Ezekiel, the prophet described the terror of "the word of the Lord" coming upon him. Ezekiel saw a whirlwind and fire, four creatures with wings, and wheels thundering down from the sky. "The appearance of the wheels and their work *was* like unto the colour of a beryl: and they four had one likeness: and their appearance and their work *was* as it were a wheel in the middle of a wheel."[1] When he saw this vision, Ezekiel fell to the ground. A voice told him to stand, and the spirit entered into him and brought him to his feet.

Perhaps Chris was destined to become a visionary or healer of some kind, if he could first heal himself. I couldn't claim to know what his calling might be; my job was to help him fulfill his potential in a world in which all prophets were madmen and no madmen were prophets.

Medical doctors don't have all the answers. As theories about the causes of disease change, the recommended course of treatment also changes. I'd be the happiest mother in the world if the psychiatric profession could solve the mystery of schizophrenia and provide an easy answer, a remedy that would resolve Chris's problems and produce no harmful side effects. But I no longer expected a simple solution. I was learning to embrace complexity, to be satisfied by small signs of progress.

I needed to get serious about preparing for the next decade of my life. I'd need to be in top form if I hoped to be able to go the distance. An energetic tune-up with Doctor Blaen seemed like a good place to start. Chris had to return for his follow-up appointment anyway.

I decided to have my assemblage point centered the traditional way, using the shaman's blow. I also wanted to get a gem lamp treatment to revitalize my liver, which was, undoubtedly, sluggish from all the red wine I'd been drinking.

Ten days after Chris's assemblage point shift, we were back in Crediton. The procedure was much like before; Tom again collected us at the train station, and again we hurtled through the hedgerows in his tiny car to get to the garden shed in time for our appointment.

Chris's assemblage point was intact, so he only got a gem treatment (with the diamond and carnelian transducer) to boost his overall energy.

Doctor Blaen found that my assemblage point had traveled up the panic-and-anxiety line on the right side of my chest. After locating it, she handed me over to Tom, who asked me to stand with my back to him. He told me to tighten my sphincter and hold my breath, and then he delivered one quick thump to my right shoulder blade, catching me off guard. I emitted a little squeak as the air reflexively left my lungs.

So, that's the famous shaman's blow! I thought as I recovered from the shock.

With my assemblage point back in its rightful place, I hoisted myself onto the examining table and stretched out on my back. Doctor Blaen handed me a large, heavy quartz-crystal wand[2] that I struggled to keep upright over the center of my chest for twenty minutes as the gem lamp's transducer pumped emerald vibrations to my liver.

While lying in this ludicrous pose, I asked Doctor Blaen if she'd heard about Prince Charles's keynote address that he'd delivered to the World Health Organization a couple of days earlier, in which he'd stated his belief that national health systems should take more account of alternative treatments such as homeopathy and acupuncture. Doctor Blaen confided to me that there was growing concern among established Harley Street doctors because some members of the Royal Family were seeing homeopathic doctors and other alternative medical practitioners on a regular basis. I laughed, my mind flashing back to a tabloid image of Princess Diana, smiling and waving to the press after having her colon irrigated at a London clinic.

Mindful of the ceremonial aspect of the treatment I was receiving, I returned my thoughts to the garden shed. Even if I hadn't traveled to some remote village in Siberia or Africa, the assemblage point shift was still a sacred ceremony, and Doctor Blaen was a shamanic healer. Shamans are not recluses who shun society. They live and work in a particular time and place, expanding upon the methods and techniques passed on to them from those who have come before.

I heard a snap as the gem lamp shut off and the electronic pulsing stopped. Doctor Blaen gently nudged me to let me know that my treatment was finished. Chris and I thanked her and Tom and gathered up our belongings for the ride back to the station. With some disappointment, I realized that we were probably leaving this particular kind of magic behind in Devon for good, but we would, indeed, see the Blaens again, several months later.

As Angela Blaen had predicted, over the next few weeks Chris began to express his thoughts and convictions more. At first, his efforts were hardly noticeable, but gradually he started to voice small preferences (peas, please, instead of carrots!) and seemed more willing, if not quite eager, to initiate a dialogue.

For years, I'd attributed my son's passivity to his temperament and personality; Chris was just the quiet, unassuming type. On occasion he would surprise me. One evening, when he was nine or ten, he pulled a chair up to the kitchen table to join me for a cup of tea, a red bandana wrapped around his head, and told me all about what he'd done that day. That kind of cozy sharing was unusual. Chris became a bit more outgoing in high school, but then he retreated into a private world, and I had to ask a lot of questions to get any kind of response out of him. Now, he was finally starting to come out of his shell.

I found that a new "me" was emerging as well. I had always been too practical, cautious, and efficient for my own liking. Rather than appreciate these qualities—and *do* something with them—I'd allowed myself to get stuck in the drudgery of daily life, waiting for someone to bestow something special on me, for something wonderful to happen to me, for life to push me in a particular direction. Funnily enough, and rather late in life, my oldest son had done just that. Chris's illness catapulted me over the rainbow. In the process, I'd discovered a *purpose*.

The seeds had been planted during my first trip to Crediton and were beginning to sprout. Idle musings developed into a viable plan: I would write a book about healing schizophrenia from the perspective of a mother who observed the whole process—a persistent mother who took notes and played detective and knew her son better than he knew himself. She would help him piece together an identity while, at the same time, embracing in herself the qualities she had previously underestimated. She would change. (The son would find his purpose too, of course.) With this book, I would describe what approaches had worked for us and show people that schizophrenia can be an invitation to an incredible healing adventure for those souls game enough to appreciate the journey.

This sense of purpose has given my life greater meaning, though the practicalities of carrying out my plan have seemed daunting at times. I knew that I would need to start a blog, build a following, and learn about the best ways to utilize social media. I'd have to find an editor and a publisher and maybe an agent. (I'd also need to learn how to write a book!)

But, first, I had some decisions to make. Was I prepared to expose my vulnerabilities and shortcomings and write honestly about mistakes I'd made? If sharing Chris's story—and my own—would help others, the answer was "Yes!"

I recognized that I might be roundly criticized for writing about my observations from the sidelines. I'm a parent, not a psychiatric patient. But that doesn't make me a mere bystander. As a parent, I know a great deal about my children. I also know how much effect parents have on their children's development. We steer them in the directions we think they should go. And with advertising by pharmaceutical companies now targeting consumers as much as doctors (in the U.S., anyway[3]), most of us can't help but be influenced by mainstream views about treatment approaches. ("Got a problem? There's a pill for that!")

I was discovering that recovery requires a journey to the self, not a trip to the pharmacy. If sharing our story would introduce parents to a new paradigm—a new mindset that could inspire the sense of awe that I was experiencing, then I was willing to accept the challenge.

Chapter 27

Hearing Voices ✳

"YOU SHOULD THINK ABOUT making friends with your voices, like I do with mine," one young man suggested to another during a family circle meeting.

On the other side of the room, Nurse Calvert and Doctor Tissot exchanged worried glances.

"Oh no, you must not do that!" Nurse Calvert said.

Doctor Tissot nodded his head in agreement. "You must ignore them!"

An awkward silence followed. That was the last time anybody talked about hearing voices during my time in the family circle.

In clinical settings, voices are almost always considered a sign of schizophrenia, and I quickly learned that the subject was off-limits. Patients and their families should only listen to the voices of experience and authority: the psychiatrists.

The HOPE staff's denial of the validity of voices was one more mark against it in my book. I was, by now, familiar with the Hearing Voices Movement, which offered an alternative and more sensible view: voices, visions, and "related phenomena" are "meaningful experiences that can be understood in many ways; hearing voices is not, in itself, an indication of illness – but difficulties coping with voices can cause great distress."[1]

Challenging the psychiatrist's specialized expertise was discouraged, and not just about hallucinations (whether visual or auditory). Questioning accepted views about the causes (and treatment) of schizophrenia was not welcome; therefore, most parents and patients remained silent in the family circle.

After reading up on the possible medical causes of schizophrenia, I asked Doctor Tissot if he thought excess copper (histapenia) could cause schizophrenia. He responded: "No one knows what causes schizophrenia."

His statement was technically correct; no one factor has been determined to cause schizophrenia. But his answer disregarded the possibility that the cause can be determined—and addressed—in individual cases. Excess copper was, apparently, just another theory that was of no relevance to Doctor Tissot. End of discussion.

With the exception of street drugs, the doctors at HOPE showed no interest in possible causes of psychosis. Periodically, a speaker was invited to the family circle—someone connected with the local hospital, the Geneva police drug intervention brigade, or the social services network—to warn about the dangers of marijuana and other recreational drugs. One such talk prompted an outburst from a normally timid mother who shouted at the staff, "My daughter never used pot or other drugs! Why are you constantly focusing on them?"

I didn't doubt that drug use among young people was a problem in Geneva, as it is in other places, or that drug abuse had probably played a role in the onset of psychosis for some of the patients at HOPE, but I, too, was frustrated by the complete lack of effort to understand the origin of psychosis in those individuals who, like my son, who had not experimented with recreational drugs.

I once asked Doctor Tissot: "To your knowledge, has anyone in the history of this program safely stopped taking their psychiatric medications?"

"Well, yes," he answered. "A few years ago, two of our young patients who'd fallen into psychosis by using street drugs were taken off their medications. Successful withdrawal can happen under these circumstances."

Apparently, my son had no chance of getting off medication because he had the wrong kind of psychosis.

Life can be so unfair, I thought. Young people who play around with recreational drugs manage to recover without long-term use of pharmaceuticals, but the kids who suffer from the same symptoms without ever having taken street drugs are doomed to a lifetime of prescription drugs. *The irony . . .*

Other drugs were also linked to the onset of psychosis, I learned. I made a remark in the family circle about the acne medication that had been prescribed for Chris when he was about sixteen. After the meeting, one of the mothers approached me.

"Have you ever made a connection between the acne medication and Chris's psychosis?" she asked. She told me the drug had been linked to depression, suicide, and psychosis and had been taken off the market.

"I am very, very angry with Doctor Tissot," the mother continued, "for not being open-minded enough to consider that THAT DRUG may have caused my daughter's psychosis. Instead, he insists that she has a psychosis of unknown origin!"

I didn't think the acne drug had caused Chris's psychosis, but pharmaceutical medications can have all kinds of side effects, so I couldn't rule out the possibility.

I did a little research and learned that acne can be a sign of pellagra, a condition caused by vitamin B deficiency.[2] According to Doctor Hoffer, acne (like pellagra—and schizophrenia) can be alleviated by taking high doses of niacin in combination with other vitamins. (Could a niacin supplement have prevented Chris from sliding into psychosis? I'll probably never know.)

The emphasis on "educating" us about the dangers of street drugs wasn't my only complaint about the way the HOPE program was managed. I disliked the frequent intrusions by the representatives of the wider medical and social welfare community. It seemed like every other week a new "guest" was introduced at the circle—a researcher or someone involved in a drug prevention program or a visiting doctor from another treatment program. These visitors didn't contribute anything to the group; they were there to observe us. Even I felt like a lab rat, causing me to wonder how Chris must have felt.

Sitting in the family circle one Tuesday in May 2006, bored out of my mind, I knew I'd reached the end of the road with HOPE. I'd had enough of the mainstream view of psychiatry. My patience had run out. I decided to trust the voice in my own head.

Halfway through the meeting, I stood up and addressed the group. In halting French, I said:

> To be truthful, all I'm interested in is curing my own son, not cheering on everybody else's child, because I don't believe that one person's success can be taken as a sign that my son or your daughter will get well in this program. Everyone here is different, but the drugs are all the same. I know that some people are going to graduate from this program more quickly than others, but that can make the ones who are still here look hopeless and their families feel worse about their prognosis.

I was pretty sure I wasn't the only parent there who had felt that way at some time or other.

After my impassioned speech, Ian and I walked out, never to return. We were done with the family circle. (Chris stayed for the rest of the meeting and then came home.)

I had an idea of where I planned to go next, but getting there was going to be complicated.

Chapter 28

Fleeting-Improvised Men ✳

EARLY IN JUNE 2006, Chris's last month at the HOPE program, Ian, Chris, and I met with Doctor Tissot, and I argued the never-ending medication point one last time.

I was getting that "Please, dear, for once don't bring up the meds" look from Ian, but I persisted. In the back of my mind, I thought that Doctor Tissot was planning to do something extravagant to demonstrate to us why Chris's medication needed to be raised.

My suspicions were justified. In the midst of our discussion, Doctor Tissot turned away from us to focus on a place high up the wall to which Chris's gaze kept returning. With quiet, dramatic flourish, he asked, "Chris, what do you see?"

"Uh, someone over there near the window."

Surprise, surprise, I thought.

Chris was seeing people in the room that no one else saw. He was hallucinating. (Instead of the term "hallucination," I prefer the way Daniel Paul Schreber describes people populating the corners of his gaze. In his book, *Memoirs of My Nervous Illness,* written at the start of the twentieth century while Schreber was an institutionalized

142

psychiatric patient, he refers to "fleeting-improvised" men—souls temporarily given human shape "by divine miracle."[1])

"Yes, Doctor Tissot," I said, "but in the family circle we're told that we shouldn't pay attention to voices. So we haven't. Of course he hears voices and sees things. Isn't that what schizophrenia is all about? The drugs haven't helped, so what good are they in Chris's case?"

On that particular day, Chris was acting more skittish than we had usually seen him, and his behavior was hard to ignore. We were stuck in this clinical program, for better or worse, and we felt obliged to humor Doctor Tissot until we could make a graceful exit. Thus, we acquiesced to his plan to raise the Solian from 200 mg to 300 mg.

Humoring Doctor Tissot, however, was becoming increasingly difficult. His pessimistic view of schizophrenia and his glass-half-empty pronouncements depressed me.

We left the meeting with the understanding that the Solian would be raised to *no more than* 300 mg. When Chris came home the following week with a prescription for 400 mg, I immediately wrote to Doctor Tissot questioning the increase, because I thought we had agreed to 300 mg. He expressed surprise at my question.

"Perhaps I haven't made my position clear," he stated in his e-mail. "Chris suffers from very handicapping hallucinations, as confirmed from our last meeting. In view of this very painful psychotic symptomatology I proposed to increase the Solian to 400 mg and keep the Leponex at its current dosage. Since I thought we were all in agreement with this strategy, if you think that the treatment is becoming the problem and not the solution, then we should discuss it at our next meeting."

Neither Ian nor I believed that raising the meds would help Chris. At our next meeting, we prevailed; the Solian was only raised to 300 mg. Doctor Tissot acknowledged that he would probably be outnumbered by the three of us, because Chris would likely side with his parents.

That much was true, though I fervently wished my son would take a position on *something,* even if his views differed from my views or Ian's. If Chris had a preference about his treatment, I wanted him to state it, loud and clear! At this point, I was spitting-nails-angry with him for what I perceived as a lack of interest in his own health. I felt I'd been pussyfooting around him for far too long in an effort to minimize the tension in our household.

After the meeting, Ian went back to work, and Chris got an earful as he and I walked home together.

"Fine!" I screamed, stamping my feet on the sidewalk and waving my arms around. "Do nothing! Stay ill! I've had it! I will not sit down with Doctor Tissot one more time! You can count on that!"

After a few days, however, I realized that if I didn't attend the final meeting, Doctor Tissot had a good shot at convincing Ian (the more "reasonable" parent on these matters) that lowering Chris's medication was foolish, and he might succeed in getting agreement from Ian and Chris to raise the dosage. I took the high road and went to the meeting, which was uneventful. Doctor Tissot said the staff could continue to monitor Chris's medication until Ian and I found a new doctor to manage his care, and we gratefully accepted his offer. We had already started the search, and we knew that finding a private psychiatrist in Geneva wouldn't be a problem[2]; the difficulty would be finding someone who would be willing to work with Doctor Erika to get Chris off medication completely.

Our business concluded, we all cordially shook hands. Doctor Tissot had kind and encouraging words for each of us. Ian, ever the diplomat, touched all the right notes in his farewell, and I, somewhat tenderly and with a tinge of humor, said, "I will almost miss you, Doctor Tissot. We've been through a lot together."

I was relieved that Chris's participation in the program was coming to an end. He had been at HOPE for twenty-two months—four months longer than the usual time permitted. In spite of all the high-priced treatment he'd received since being admitted to CAMH, he hadn't recovered.

The cost of his treatment was staggering. From January 2004 to June 2006, a period of thirty months, our insurance company paid 341,434 CHF (Swiss francs).[3] Covered expenses included two hospitalizations (in two different countries) for a total of six months, the twenty-two months in the day program, Doctor Erika's services, prescription drugs, and laboratory tests. (Chris's vitamin regimen was not covered by insurance. Ian and I also paid for occasional family counseling sessions with Doctor Piaget.)

And yet, Chris still suffered from "very handicapping hallucinations," according to Doctor Tissot. If he was getting the best help available, then, to my mind, he should either no longer hallucinate or else, at the least, the hallucinations should have diminished. Chris should look well and act well and be ready to think about a vocation.

Fortunately for us, more and more people were sharing their stories about recovering without drugs, and I knew that there had to be treatments that would support Chris as his dosages were reduced. I wasn't interested in just managing his symptoms and behaviors; I believed that such surface manifestations would change when the root causes of his illness were addressed—and resolved.

Convinced that drugs were an impediment to my son's recovery, I wanted him off all of them. However, I was beginning to realize that recovery wasn't going to happen quickly, or by using only one approach. Recovery wasn't an event; it was a process, and I was in for the long haul.

Chapter 29

Family Constellations ✻

IAN AND I paid a visit to our family doctor to see if he would be willing to help Chris get off the meds. (This doctor had prescribed Paxil for me when Chris was first hospitalized. If he could prescribe antidepressants, I reasoned, then maybe he could prescribe antipsychotics as well.) But, like most of his medical peers, our doctor considered schizophrenia a chronic brain disease, and he believed that Chris would need medication for the remainder of his life. He said he wasn't comfortable taking Chris on as a psychiatric patient, but he'd be happy to continue seeing him for checkups or lab work, as he had done in the past.

Though this pessimistic view about Chris's prognosis troubled me, I didn't have the energy to change family doctors. I turned my attention to finding a psychiatrist who would be willing to work with Doctor Erika. In particular, I wanted to find a psychiatrist trained in Family Constellation work,[1] and I hoped that such a person would also be open-minded enough to help Chris move away from reliance on the drugs.

Family Constellation work was developed by Bert Hellinger, a German psychotherapist and former Jesuit priest who spent many years living amongst the Zulu people in South Africa. It is based on the premise that patterns of behavior can be carried forward, especially if a family member experienced loss or injustice in an earlier generation.[2] Constellation work is designed to help participants resolve the issues and thereby avoid perpetuating destructive patterns.[3]

After pursuing several false leads, someone told me that the head of the HOPE program, Doctor Rx, was the best person to speak to about Family Constellation therapy. *Wait a minute! Doctor Rx?* Had Doctor Rx been withholding information about alternative treatments from us the entire time Chris had been in the HOPE program? What had we been doing for those twenty-two months—paddling around in the shallow end of the psychosis wading pool? I found this latest twist on my convoluted journey ironic, but I had no intention of contacting Doctor Rx.

I finally found what I was looking for, with the help of Doctor Piaget, who referred me to Maria Stern, MD, a trilingual psychiatrist and psychotherapist with a strong Family Constellation practice in Geneva. I telephoned her and explained why I thought Family Constellation work might help Chris. I also asked her views on pharmaceutical drugs. She believed that neuroleptics, if necessary, should be used sparingly, in low doses, and, ideally, only for a short duration. "But I prefer to think of myself as more of a psychotherapist than a psychiatrist," she added.

I scheduled an initial appointment in late June, thinking that Chris might be ready to try a new approach after he finished the HOPE program.

At the end of June, Ian, Chris, and I walked up the stairs of a small residential building near the Hôpital Cantonal de Genève and rang the doorbell. We heard a scuffling sound, followed by an eerie moment of silence as we were observed through the peephole. Apparently, Doctor Stern worked alone.

We all took a step back while the door was unchained and swung open. "Good morning everyone." Doctor Stern extended her right arm to shake hands with each of us as we filed into the large room. "You are right on time."

"Yes, we are learning to be more like the Swiss," Ian joked.

Doctor Stern smiled. Gesturing to a loveseat and two chairs grouped around a small glass table in a corner of the room, she invited us to sit down. The space was otherwise bare, save for three large Oriental carpets that covered most of the parquet floor.

While Ian chatted with Doctor Stern about the best place to park our car in the future, I sized her up. Fortysomething. Formal European English, Germanic diction. She wore no jewelry or makeup and was conservatively dressed in a pearl-gray suit and a light-blue blouse. Her careful choice of words made her seem sincere. I hoped she would prove to be a good psychotherapist for Chris.

After more small talk, Doctor Stern turned her attention to Chris and tried to get him to share a little about himself. Chris avoided looking directly at her, and several times Doctor Stern had to ask him to repeat himself because he spoke so softly and hesitantly.

Satisfied that Chris was there of his own free will, Doctor Stern asked how much we knew about Family Constellations. I surprised her by handing her a narrative summary of our family's history, starting with Chris, Alex, and Taylor and going back four generations (up to and including Ian's and my grandparents).

"My clients aren't usually so well prepared," Doctor Stern said with a smile. She promised to review our family history before our next appointment.

"Chris helped me with the research," I said, casting a motherly beam in his direction. Chris and I had constructed our family tree over the course of the previous year. Searching through family records and Internet databases for information about the births and deaths of our ancestors was a bonding experience, a chance to talk about our relatives and imagine what their lives may have been like.

Chris looked up at the mention of his name and then returned to staring at the floor.

"Oh, that's nice to hear," said Doctor Stern. "It is good to get to know our relatives. The sooner the better."

"Normally," she explained to the three of us, "I conduct my Family Constellation therapy with several families at once. The participants stand in for each other's families as we enact each client's constellation. But that is done in French, so I will schedule an appointment for just your family. I will be the stand-in for your relatives, who will be represented by paper shoes."

Ian and I looked at each other. *Shoes?*

"Let me show you what I mean. Wait here," Doctor Stern said before disappearing through a door to her office. She soon reappeared with a file folder containing the outlines of pairs of shoes that represented various people.

"This constellation concerned the family of a man I saw last month," Doctor Stern said as she laid a sheet of paper bearing shoeprints and the word "CHILD" on the floor in the center of the room. "The Child's shoes represented my client," she said. "He placed the shoeprints of his parents above him, creating a triangle."

Doctor Stern laid a sheet of paper labeled "MOTHER" and another labeled "FATHER" on the floor. Each pair of shoes was placed about a yard from the Child's shoes.

"This is a conventional arrangement, normally without tension," Doctor Stern explained, "but in this case, the man put his grandmother *here*."

Doctor Stern placed the Grandmother's shoeprints directly between the Mother's shoes and the Father's shoes.

"She meddled in their lives, which caused a lot of problems. How can a husband and wife communicate with a mother-in-law in the way?"

Doctor Stern paused to give us time to study the pattern of shoeprints on the floor.

"Once the shoes are arranged," she continued, "I take over as the actor, stepping into the shoes of each person."

She took a few steps backward and stood on top of the paper labeled CHILD.

"As a representative of that person, I sense the hidden connections, issues, and patterns that have characterized the energy field of the family. I see how those patterns and issues have affected each member of the family. But I also use my intuition, and I say whatever comes into my mind. You will sometimes observe my body move in response to the energy I am feeling."

Doctor Stern returned to her chair. Looking first at Ian and then at me, she said, "When I am finished, I will ask you to take over and step into the shoes of your family members. You may choose to rearrange the shoes based on the insights you've gained."

"How can this therapy help someone resolve a conflict or heal emotionally and physically when the other family members aren't physically present during the session?" Ian asked.

"Those who *are* present are affected by observing or participating in the constellation. We can sense how and where the injustices and exclusions have occurred," Doctor Stern explained.

The act of rearranging the shoes creates a symbolic change in the family dynamics, Doctor Stern told us. Healing can then happen because the energy of the constellation begins to flow naturally in the bodies and minds of the participants.

"The healing energy radiates outward to absent family members," Doctor Stern said.

Ian and I looked at each other and nodded. Doctor Stern's description was consistent with my understanding of Constellation work.

My back was stiff from sitting so long. I discreetly pushed up my sleeve to check my watch. Two and a half hours had elapsed, and it was time to go. Ian, Doctor Stern, and I got out our calendars and settled on two appointments for the whole family in the first week of July.

Alex and Taylor read the short write-up of our family history that I had given to Doctor Stern, but they were not especially interested in people they'd never met, and they came to the first session of Constellation therapy under duress. They were, understandably, unhappy about the turmoil our family had gone through because of Chris. Alex announced at the start that he was "too busy" to make it to the next appointment. (A born executive.) Taylor remained aloof throughout the session.

Doctor Stern asked Ian and me to decide which family members the first constellation would be about. "If they are on the maternal side," she said, looking in my direction, "then you will put the shoes on the floor. If they are on the paternal side," she said, turning to Ian, "then you will."

Ian and I had agreed before we arrived that we would start with his father's side of the family.

Ian is named after his paternal grandfather, Ian John Forbes, who left Aberdeen, Scotland for Toronto in 1914 at the age of seventeen. When war broke out shortly thereafter, John (as he was known) joined a Toronto regiment, whereupon he was shipped first to England and then to France.

John's military records indicate that he was in hospital most of the time he was in France, suffering from pyrexia of unknown origin (PUO), or what was commonly called "trench fever." A patient usually recovered from trench fever in less than a month, but, in rare cases, the aftereffects persisted. The symptoms included fatigue, anxiety, headache, neuralgia, and depressed mood.

After returning to Toronto, John lived as a semi-invalid. His wife, Emma, was an English nurse who had worked in hospitals in Southern Ontario before her marriage, so it's possible that she met her husband when he was a patient and just back from the war. Their four children (two boys and two girls) were all born several years after the war ended.

John and Emma's two sons were both named David William. The first died of leukemia; the second (Bill) married Joan and had four children. My husband, Ian, is the oldest. Bill and Joan's acrimonious divorce during Ian's teen years strained his relationship with both of them.

Doctor Stern urged Ian to be spontaneous when placing the shoe outlines on the floor. "The placement should be intuitive, not logical," she said. "Don't think too much."

Ian laid out six pairs of shoeprints, representing his Grandparents (John and Emma), his Father (Bill), his Aunts (Maude, Bill's twin sister, and Margaret), and his Uncle (the first David William).

When he had finished laying out the shoes, Ian sat next to me on the loveseat. We waited nervously to see what would happen next.

Doctor Stern began a mesmerizing narrative dance, stepping first into the shoes of Ian's Grandfather. She stood quietly for about a minute, her head bowed. Her arms hung limply by her sides, a dangling marionette.

"Hmmph," she said, inhaling sharply through her nostrils. Her shoulders shivered ever so slightly. The room was completely silent; all eyes were focused on Doctor Stern. After shaking herself a little more, she began to speak from the perspective of Ian's Grandfather.

"I can see that I have three lovely children, but I am not close to any of them. I have a fine wife, but I can only see part of her from where I am standing. Where is my firstborn son, David William?"

With her feet planted firmly, Doctor Stern rotated her body and gazed over her left shoulder, continuing in her role as Ian's Grandfather.

"Oh, there he is. He was so young when he died." To his wife, Emma, "Grandfather" softly said, "I see that you are standing by him. You haven't forgotten him. We gave his name to our next son, didn't we, dear?"

Ian and I each grabbed a couple of tissues from a large dispenser on the glass table and began dabbing at our eyes. As the drama progressed, we wept openly. We were heartbroken that ill health, grief over the death of his firstborn child, and whatever other personal demons had plagued Ian's grandfather had caused him to become estranged from his wife and children.

Doctor Stern wept, too. (Taylor and Alex were dry-eyed and looked bored, occasionally exchanging suppressed giggles.)

Every so often, Doctor Stern would glance sideways to see how Chris was following the unfolding drama. He was riveted. His eyes never strayed from Doctor Stern. He seemed to understand the dynamics of the constellation, and sensed the burden carried by its family members.

When Doctor Stern was finished with her acting role, she suggested that Ian trade places with her.

"Now it's your turn to stand in the shoes of your relatives and to experience something about their lives. After speaking from the perspective of each person, you are free to rearrange the shoes based on your new understandings and insight."

When he stood in his Father's shoes, Ian realized that he couldn't see the almost-forgotten David William from where he was standing.

He moved his Uncle's shoes out from behind his Grandfather and placed them next to his Father (Bill, David William's younger brother and namesake). Next, while standing in his Grandfather's shoes, Ian felt a desire to be closer to his wife. He moved Emma's shoes closer to John's.

"How do you feel about the family?" Doctor Stern asked each of us in turn.

Ian felt immensely sad, he said, but more understanding of his relatives. So did I, and so did Chris. Taylor and Alex mechanically stated that they felt a bit sad, too. I'm sure that what they said was true. Sorrow hung in the air; even they could not ignore the shift that had occurred.

After three hours, we were all exhausted and ready to leave.

Doctor Stern cautioned against overanalyzing what we'd seen and heard. "Don't speak too much about it, to each other or to other people. Whatever comes out of these sessions will happen at an emotional level and will take time."

Two days later, we were back in Doctor Stern's office, save for Alex, who had resolutely clung to the commitments he claimed he could not possibly break. All the pleading in the world got us nowhere.

"Alex is tough like that," I remarked to Doctor Stern.

She smiled and said, "Being tough is probably a good way to be."

She asked for our thoughts about the previous session. Ian and I both said we felt saddened by the experience, but we felt closer to Ian's family on his father's side than we had before. Chris nodded his head in agreement; Taylor nodded, too.

When my turn came, I chose to work with my mother's side of the family because of the impact the early death of my grandmother had had on my mother. (I could have started with my father's side for the same reason; my paternal grandfather had died when my father was eight years old. I decided to focus on the maternal side because my mother had told me about the troubled relationship she'd had with her father, whereas most of what my father shared about his upbringing was positive.)

My mother, Lily, was only four years old when her mother (Anna) died, in 1924, of scarlet fever—which she had caught from Lily. (Anna had been the second wife of Lily's father, Kurt. Kurt married two more women after Anna and lived well into his seventies.)

A cabinet maker, Kurt was transferred from the Philadelphia area to Montreal soon after Anna died. Lily and her older brother (Norman) were supervised by a series of housekeepers, one of whom became Kurt's third wife when Lily was a teenager. (That marriage was short-lived.) My mother used to say that wife number four, who was the same age as my mother, was more than happy to take orders from Kurt and that's why their marriage lasted until Kurt's death.

My mother was kind and loving, but she made no attempt to soften her feelings about her father. While I was growing up, I occasionally heard about how my grandfather had forced my mother to quit high school because she'd failed to get a scholarship to pay for her books. (Only the top student in the class was given a scholarship, and my mother's rank had slipped to second place that year.) She was sent to a commercial college and entered the workforce at sixteen without a high school diploma. Once she started earning money, Kurt took her entire paycheck.

Toward the end of her life, my mother shared with me her belief that her father blamed her for her mother's death. That made sense to me, knowing the humiliations she'd endured. "Never marry a man you don't respect," she advised my sisters and me. Clearly, she loved and respected my father.

Though I'd met my grandfather twice—once when I was about three years old and once when I was a teenager—my impressions of him derived mostly from old family photographs. At my parents' wedding in 1948 (with Wife Number Four), Kurt was dressed in a dark pinstripe suit and a Homburg hat. He struck me as both a ladies' man and a natty dresser.

I quickly laid out the shoes for my Grandfather Kurt, Grandmother Anna, Mother Lily, and Uncle Norman. I also included in the constellation my grandfather's first wife, Edith, who was also his cousin. Edith died (childless) when she was twenty. A Family Constellation therapist might say that her death enabled my grandmother to marry my grandfather, and that's why she should be included in the family grouping. I did not include Kurt's third or fourth wives.

The pattern was a conventional one: Grandparents placed on the same linear path, about three feet apart, shoes facing their children (Lily and Norman). I placed Edith several feet behind my Grandfather and returned to my seat.

Doctor Stern took her position as interpreter of family dramas. She stepped into Mother Lily's shoes, and, in a plaintive voice, asked, "Where is my mother?"

As I watched and listened, I realized that, as a child, I had never given much thought to the effect of Anna's death on four-year-old Lily. I knew the loss was significant for my mother, but I had accepted my grandmother's early death as one of those things that so often happened to people of my parents' generation. She had died; that was all. I didn't dwell on it. Now, I felt the gravity of the situation. I sensed that I was about to discover some disturbing truth that I had not fully grasped before. I felt cold, despite the warm summer air wafting in through the open window.

Next, Doctor Stern took the place of my Grandfather. She hung her head, dropped her shoulders in the marionette position, and said nothing for a few minutes; then, slowly, a look of horror came over her. She put her hands over her cheeks and shook her head in dismay while rocking slightly back and forth. She said nothing. She didn't need to say anything. My Grandfather had already lost his first wife; now, his second wife was also gone. He was left with two young children to raise.

Doctor Stern stepped into Edith's shoes and asked, with a combination of hurt and anger in her voice, "Doesn't anyone remember me?"

As the constellation unfolded, I thought of an old black-and-white photograph of me and my sisters that had been taken on Christmas Day. Our faces looked as sullen as rain clouds. Our parents had bought us all kinds of dolls as Christmas presents—Tiny Tears baby dolls and glamorous fashion dolls with frothy tulle skirts. These gifts would have thrilled lots of other girls, but not us. We weren't interested in nurturing or being nurtured, and, for whatever reason, we pushed our mother away. We didn't want to be close to her, physically or emotionally. Of the three of us, I was the only one who had children. My sisters were childless by choice.

Doctor Stern became very still. "I sense a chill in the room," she said. "It feels like death." She pulled her light, cotton cardigan a little closer to her body. I reached for a tissue and wiped my eyes, suddenly remembering another family member who had died early, my (maternal) great-grandmother, Clara. The pieces started to fall into place. A family pattern had started with Clara's death:

> Anna was ten when her mother, Clara, died;
> Anna was able to marry Kurt because Edith had died;
> Anna's daughter, Lily, (my mother) was four when her mother died.

When I was three years old, I almost died from a blood disorder. (Was I trying to sacrifice myself to save my mother from an early death?) Unsettling thoughts about the mother–child bond continued to pop into my head as the constellation drew to completion.

Perhaps my sisters and I refused to show my mother physical affection because we feared that if we got too close something bad would happen. Or maybe she unconsciously feared that she would die young and sent off messages that we shouldn't get too close to her.

What effect had this pattern had on my relationships with my children? I wondered.

I remembered all those sleepless nights after Chris was born, when he cried and cried because I had no breast milk. He was literally starving, denied the most nurturing food of all.

I felt sick with remorse.

During this constellation, as in the first one, Doctor Stern looked up at Chris from time to time to gauge his reactions. At the end of the session, she suddenly declared, "I think I've got it!" Turning to Chris, she said, "You should not have to carry this burden any longer." Without further explanation, she announced that the session was over.

For the second time, we left Doctor Stern's office feeling exhausted.

We were deeply aware of the sacrifices that had been made by our relatives. Abiding by Doctor Stern's instructions, we did not discuss what had taken place during the session. Each of us was left to find meaning in what we had witnessed, in our own way.

We would have to wait, and let the magic happen.

Chapter 30

Superman ✳

ANY BENEFIT Chris may have received from our Family Constellation sessions was overshadowed by his descent into a horrific state soon after the therapy was over. My faith in his ability to recover was sorely tested, and I wondered if he would ever get well.

At his parents' suggestion, Chris enrolled in a summer course to improve his French language skills. He expressed interest and seemed enthusiastic at the prospect of attending class again on a daily basis. He may have been humoring us, but Ian and I didn't see any downside. Class size was small, and the course only lasted three weeks. We thought it would be a good opportunity for Chris to stick a toe back into a classroom and see how he liked being in school. He hadn't been in an academic setting since attending Webster when he was a patient in the HOPE program.

He completed the two-hour placement exam (a feat in itself), and at first he came home cheerful and happy to talk about his day. Soon, however, his confidence, which was shaky under the best of circumstances, plummeted. Perhaps the expectation of classroom participation was too much for him; perhaps he wasn't yet ready to venture beyond the safety of his home environment on his own.

On the morning of the third day of the course, Ian and Chris took the same bus. Ian watched as an attractive young woman sat down next to Chris and started to chat. Staring straight ahead, Chris slumped in his seat, ignoring the woman and avoiding eye contact. He came home from class that evening, headed straight to his bedroom, and lay on his bed. I asked him if he was okay and got no response; he just stared at the ceiling.

For the next two days, Chris moved in slow motion. He was late getting to class, and he didn't respond at all when I spoke to him, as if his mind had vacated his body. The following week, he dropped the course.

I maintained, halfheartedly, that this latest setback was yet another bump on the road to wellness, and I tried not to allow the sudden change in Chris's behavior to throw me off course, but watching his condition deteriorate so rapidly dashed some of my hopes for his future.

The night after the bus incident, the two of us went to see *Superman Returns* at our local cinema. Fantasy and sci-fi have never interested me, but I know they are genres that Chris likes. Though I worried a bit at times that indulging his fantasies might further weaken his hold on reality, I reasoned that small, measured amounts would do no harm and might even be beneficial, in much the same way that the nanodoses of substances used in homeopathic remedies are thought to promote healing, whereas larger doses of the same substances are more likely to produce undesirable symptoms.

Chris's eyes were glued to the screen for the entire film. As Superman struggled to overturn a crystallized landmass that threatened to end life on earth, I whispered, "Hey, I'm enjoying this movie, too," but the roar of the continent being lifted up drowned out my attempts at small talk.

Watching the film, I was struck by the resemblance between Chris in his deteriorated condition and Superman when he was exposed to green kryptonite—helpless, enfeebled, stripped of his powers, hovering in a twilight zone between life and death. In my mind, Chris *is* a kind of superhero. He has exceptional intuitive capabilities and huge reservoirs of empathy and compassion that enable him to achieve oneness with All-That-Is. He understands that the destructive forces in the universe might cause the world to end—by fire or by ice.

As we left the theater, I wondered how I could help Chris return to earth, as Superman had done after a long absence from our planet. Chris would have to learn how to channel his gifts in ways that strengthened him. He would have to learn resilience so that he could cope when people, situations, and substances weakened him.

I had no expertise in giving wise counsel to superheroes. I was continually on the lookout for some real-life magic that would help him stay present in the here-and-now. Shifting his assemblage point had produced good results initially, but it hadn't prevented this latest decline.

Chris would remain in a feeble state for several more months, during which time he looked and acted as if he was hovering somewhere nearer to death than to life—pale, sad, and eerily uncommunicative. Perhaps he was anticipating our upcoming family vacation, which, in the course of getting to know our ancestors, brought us all a little closer to the topic of death.

Chapter 31

✳ *Mother, Heal Thyself*

THE EMOTIONAL IMPACT of the Family Constellation sessions caused Ian and me to appreciate the sacrifices of our grandparents. As a way of honoring those who had fought in the twentieth century's two world wars (including Ian's paternal grandfather and a cousin on my father's side), we spent our summer vacation driving to war memorials in France and Belgium.

In early August, we wedged Chris, Alex, and Taylor into the back seat of our Honda CR-V and set out for the battlefields of northern France. We had no idea where in France Ian's grandfather had been stationed during the Great War, as his military records did not disclose this information, but we thought he might have been at Vimy.

The beautiful, haunting, World War I memorial of Vimy is owned and managed by the Canadian government. The site incorporates large areas of pasture that are roped off to the public because of the unexploded munitions that lie beneath the surface. Our knowledgeable tour guide told us that a very young Adolph Hitler had been at Vimy, delivering messages to the German front line.

We entered underground tunnels with passageways so narrow that the soldiers were forced to stand all night, waiting to charge the enemy lines in the early morning hours.

Like cattle in line for the slaughterhouse, I thought.

Most of those young men did not survive the horrors of the dawn. If Ian's grandfather saw action at Vimy and lived, then he was one of the lucky ones.

The many charms of the old provincial capital of Arras, where we spent the night, were lost on Taylor and Alex. They got the scare of their lives when they ventured down the darkened streets behind the town square and were approached by two young thugs, who roughed them up a bit while warning, "Never come back to Arras if you know what's good for you!"

Taylor and Alex broke away and ran back to our hotel, arriving breathless and shaken. "From now on, we're sticking with you guys!" they told us.

In the morning, I bought plastic flowers wrapped in cellophane to leave at the grave of my father's cousin, Bryce. The Adegem Canadian War Cemetery, where Bryce was buried, was located in Belgium, a short distance from Arras.

"Look," Alex said when we arrived in Adegem, "a Canada War Museum. Someone there will know how to get to the cemetery."

We stepped inside the small museum and chatted with a friendly young woman at the information booth. On learning that we were Canadians, she told us a story as she handed each of us a souvenir chocolate bar bearing a bright red maple leaf on the wrapper.

"In 1944, a number of Canadian regiments arrived in Adegem, which was then a town of about three thousand inhabitants, and they stayed for several weeks. They had very little clothing to wear, really only what they had on, so people in the town used to invite them into their houses and do their laundry for them. Well, you can imagine what happened next. Nine months after the regiments left, the town population swelled to thirty-four hundred inhabitants. We call them the lover boys," the young woman said with an impish grin. "They gave out chocolates for a kiss, and I guess they got a little more than a kiss in return."

We laughed and thanked her for the story and the chocolates. The cemetery, we learned, was located about two kilometers away from the museum, down a narrow dirt road.

After parking our car outside the unlocked gate, we walked through rows of identical white gravestones extending as far as the eye could see. Threatening dark clouds hung above us.

Many of the names had faded from the gravestones, but I had retrieved the grave number and row in advance from the cemetery's website, so locating Bryce's grave was easy.

Bryce was twenty years old when he died in October 1944; he was killed while securing the Allies' supply route to Antwerp. Our family stood silently at his grave for a few minutes, and then I stepped forward and placed the flowers next to the gravestone. Ian offered up a prayer.

A light rain started to fall. Ian and I headed to our car; Alex and Taylor explored the grounds a bit further. Chris lingered by Bryce's grave with his head bowed before slowly making his way to the parking lot.

Back in France, we toured the U.S. and Canadian war memorials in Normandy and returned to Geneva in mid-August feeling sad and drained. Soon after, Alex left to start his second year at Purdue, and Taylor entered his second-to-last year of high school. Our apartment was quieter than it had been in many months.

My mother's cousin in Pennsylvania had recently sent me two black-and-white photographs—one of Anna, my maternal grandmother, and one of Anna and Kurt enjoying a light-hearted moment together in their backyard.

Before receiving the photos, I hadn't known what Anna looked like. Now I had a daily reminder of both Anna and Kurt. I realized that my grandparents' brief time together must have held moments of joy. Despite the negative impact this ill-fated couple had had on my mother, I chose to focus on the positive aspects of their relationship and erected a modest shrine to them in the living room.

In September, I planned another trip to Crediton for Chris and me. We would see Angela Blaen in November, just before Chris was scheduled to begin weekly therapy sessions with Doctor Stern.

The pretext for booking the appointment was that I wanted to get a tune-up and make sure that my assemblage point had stayed in place, but, in truth, I was pretty sure it was intact. I was becoming a bit of a journey junkie. Escaping routine and experiencing the wonders of the new was good for both Chris and me. My son had finally managed to pull himself out of the funk he'd been stuck in since July. He was looking more robust than I had seen him in a while.

When November rolled around, we followed the same itinerary as before, spending the night in Bristol and taking the train to Exeter the next day. This time, however, Chris suddenly became very weak and pale on the train.

"Mom, I'm really tired and I feel kind of sick," he mumbled, draping himself sideways across our seats.

Uh-oh, I thought. *Kryptonite again.*

Other passengers stared, and I was afraid we wouldn't be able to make it off the train, let alone board another one. I had never seen Chris in a state of complete energetic collapse! He was fine one minute and unable to function the next.

At Exeter's St. David's Station I managed to haul him off the train. I found the stationmaster's office, where Chris was invited to lie down on a bench. I left to find a bottle of water, asking myself if I had misjudged Chris's ability to undertake this journey.

When I returned, Chris was able sit up and drink some water. Then, we did some EFT sequences together to clear whatever was causing his sudden loss of power. After an hour or so, he said he felt well enough to continue. We were fortunate: the next train deposited us in Crediton just as Tom pulled up in his car.

The appointment with Angela Blaen went well. She checked our assemblage points, which were positioned where they were supposed to be.

Lying on the table, getting my liver energized with an emerald transducer while my son sat watching from a chair in the corner of the room, I wondered if perhaps we were spending a little too much time together. *The goal, after all, is independence!* I thought.

I thanked Doctor Blaen for her help, and then Tom drove Chris and me back to the train station.

The return leg of the journey passed without incident. Chris showed no signs of the debilitation he'd experienced that morning. As our plane departed Bristol, I thought of possible explanations for the incident on the train. Could Chris have had a simple case of motion sickness? Maybe his medication or supplements needed to be adjusted. Was there something about seeing the Blaens again that worried him? Doctor Blaen's quartz crystals had drawn him away from excessive fantasy and grounded him more firmly in the real world, a world he seemed reluctant to be part of.

I marveled at my willingness to embrace the full range of possibilities, from the mundane to the outlandish, in an effort to make sense of what was happening to Chris. Traveling to England to shift assemblage points, channeling dead ancestors, and seeing my son as a superhero were just some of the paths I'd explored in my determination to "keep an open mind."

We were halfway across the English Channel, and I was deep in my ruminations, when I decided to ask for guidance from my Higher Self. What more did I need to do to help my son? Immediately, I received an answer: Heal yourself.

I heard no loud voice, just my own mind instantly telling me what to do. *Of course!* I thought. *Before I can help another person heal, I must first heal myself.*

Soon after arriving back in Geneva, Ian and I signed up for a beginning yoga course that met one night a week. We were in our early fifties and our bodies were unaccustomed to the postures, but we persevered over the next few years, occasionally signing up for extra classes. I would liken practicing yoga, and, later, learning to meditate, to slowly letting the air out of a balloon. Bit by bit, my worry and sadness dissipated. When I awoke during the night, I was able to go back to sleep instead of lying awake thinking about Chris.

My own healing was well underway, and so was my husband's. Ian had joined me in practicing EFT, yoga, and meditation; he'd participated in the Family Constellation work, and we went together for counseling sessions with Doctor Piaget.

Our son's healing was proving to be more of a challenge. One step forward, three steps back would be a good way to describe the incremental progress Chris made. Occasionally, a leap forward gave us an indication of what was possible.

Chapter 32

✳ *Rebuilding*

CHRIS'S LONG-AWAITED BREAKTHROUGH finally happened, during the winter of 2006/2007.

A friend's daughter was living in Paris and wanted to ski the Alps. Emily spent a weekend with us in November 2006. When she invited Chris to go skiing with her on Sunday, he readily agreed.

"How was Chris?" I asked Emily when they returned.

"Quiet," she said. "He was very polite and considerate, but he only spoke to me if I spoke to him first."

I asked the same question in February, 2007, when Emily came back for another visit. Again, she'd asked Chris to join her for a day of skiing. But this time I knew her answer would be different.

"Oh, he was just great!" Emily said. "He talked with me the whole time. I didn't need to prompt him. What a big change from November!"

Chris was able to converse better, with his family and with others. The new Chris began phoning up friends he hadn't seen for years to suggest that they get together. He wanted to be around people.

The magic had happened. Sometime between November and February, seemingly from one day to the next, Chris began to act "normal." (He'd never shown such dramatic improvement while attending the HOPE program.)

Doctor Stern thought he was ready to withdraw from the two prescription drugs (Leponex and Solian) he'd been taking for three years. Doctor Erika expected the process to take about a year.

From February 2007 to March 2008, the two doctors worked together to eliminate all of Chris's drugs. Ian, Chris, and I met with Doctor Stern every three months to discuss Chris's progress; we occasionally spoke to Doctor Erika by phone. As the medications were progressively lowered, Chris's previous weight gain melted away, and he was able to exercise a bit more. He looked healthy, and he had a lot more energy. Seeing him gradually come to life was a joyful experience for Ian and me.

Buoyed by his newfound energy and joie de vivre, Chris enrolled in a month-long physics course in England in July of 2007. After convincing his parents that he was ready for the challenge of living away from home (not that we needed much convincing, as we thought his independence was long overdue), he set off for Sussex, where he would live on campus in student housing. Unfortunately, he found concentrating on his studies difficult, and the inevitable happened. He stopped going to class and didn't even attempt the final exam.

Ian and I were angry with him for blowing the opportunity. Would this be his future, unable to commit to academic or vocational work? Our consolation was the realization that Chris had experienced a social success, if not an academic one. He'd managed to live away from home—in another country, even—for an entire month, during which he made friends, bought groceries, and cooked for himself. This was progress.

Subsequently, Chris audited a couple of liberal arts courses closer to home, at Webster University. To Ian's and my delight, he also joined the church choir and started taking voice lessons once a week with the choir director. She saw in him talent worth cultivating.

"He understands music," she said. "A lot of my pupils don't. He's also got a very good voice for early church music."

Curious to know Chris's thoughts about his experience of breakdown and recovery thus far, I asked him to share his recollections.

He said that he'd felt overwhelmed at the end of high school. In his mind, he wasn't sick, just lacking in maturity. At my request, he wrote the following account in 2008:

> In ninth grade I hadn't yet reached the point where my real-world goals seemed out of reach, but in my final year in school my perception of my skills could not match my aspirations, to excel in music, be the "best" in my class at academics, or find my "niche" in the world of such skills. I was a "good student" who went to class, did his homework, and was in a rock band. Everyone else, except my drummer, was keen to go far away to university, and I was no exception. What I didn't realize at the time, and this was very important, was why I wanted to go.
>
> In high school, life seemed to be becoming just one gig after the other. Like the Goo Goo Dolls sing, I was growin' up too fast. I was at school like everyone else, and yet I wasn't there at all. At university I had many existential and religious thoughts and began to turn inward. I had "friends," some real friends for a while, but it was when I realized my lack of academic progress in science was directly in line with my "socializing," including drinking beer regularly as a habit in my new "adulthood," that I saw the writing on the wall.

While I do believe that Chris felt he was "growin' up too fast," and I agree that he might have been having a full-blown existential crisis, I'm not convinced that the reason for his lack of progress in science is plausible. For a guy who thinks he was just unsure of his future and had drunk a bit too much beer, he took us all on quite a ride. I think he was telling me what he thought I wanted to hear—that he was going to try harder, smarten up, and revert to being a "good boy" by fulfilling social expectations.

Much as I wanted to see Chris go back to school and take charge of his life, I still had a lot to learn about where this journey was taking us both. Finding an authentic life after a psychotic breakdown requires an enormous rebuilding effort that can last for years. After the shaky and crumbling old structure has collapsed, a new foundation must be laid before a new structure can be erected.

Many years had gone by, and we were still mainly working on the ground floor.

Chapter 33

✳ *The Alexander Technique*

CHRIS SEEMED TO BE doing well after he stopped taking medication, but I soon learned that achieving a lasting recovery wasn't going to be as simple as I'd once hoped.

In 2008, Chris was twenty-four years old. Ian and I tried to be understanding of his needs, but our patience was wearing thin. We thought that he was sufficiently recovered to be doing something productive with his time. People we knew who had seen Chris when he was most ill marveled at his improvement. We fervently wished he would become more independent and live on his own—preferably while earning a degree. He took a step forward and registered for two courses at Webster that would begin in October.

Encouraged by our son's progress, Ian and I searched for schools that could provide a nurturing environment for him. We discovered a small college in a tranquil mountain setting in the United States. The school offered courses in music and environmental studies and a work program.

Our plan was to take Chris for a visit during our summer vacation. If he liked what he saw—and if he did well in the courses at Webster—he might be ready to apply for admission the following year.

I realized that our enthusiasm about sending Chris off to college stemmed as much from a desire to reclaim *our* independence from Chris as from a desire to help him become more independent and self-sufficient. Taylor was leaving in August to begin his freshman year at Pennsylvania State University, and Alex was entering his senior year at Purdue. Ian and I wanted to show Chris that we believed he, too, had a promising academic future.

Doctor Stern did not share our enthusiasm. Any talk of sending Chris away from home was premature as far as she was concerned—and she was concerned. I wondered how long she was planning to keep him as a patient.

To be fair to Doctor Stern, I admit that even though I had observed great improvements in Chris, I also thought that he probably needed more time to recover before he would be ready to leave the nest. I thought he could benefit from additional holistic therapies, and I suspected he might encounter more setbacks before he could be considered "recovered." As it turned out, the next crisis was just around the corner.

Five and a half years after his acute psychotic breakdown, Chris still displayed awkwardness in social settings. He lagged behind others when walking in a group, hesitated before entering a room, and was uncertain when and how to sit down in a chair. These behaviors had persisted whether or not he was taking medication.

With Chris communicating more, his thought process was plain to see. He gave complicated answers to straightforward questions and always paused for what seemed like an eternity before opening his mouth to speak. If Alex asked him what Portugal was like when he was there in the eleventh grade, instead of answering, "Great, but very hot," or, "The people in the village where I stayed were dirt poor," or something based on his experience, Chris might reference a verse from a poem, such as *Childe Harold's Pilgrimage*. The significance would be clear to him (he would know that Lord Byron wrote the poem after traveling through Portugal and other countries), but the rest of us would be mystified.

I attributed Chris's behavior to feeling ill at ease in his own body. He needed help integrating body, mind, and spirit. I remembered that *The Natural Medicine Guide to Schizophrenia* included a chapter on cranial osteopathy,[1] and I booked craniosacral therapy sessions for both Chris and me, not realizing it was a different therapy.[2] (Both practices work with the cranial rhythm generated by the pulsing of the cerebrospinal fluids surrounding the brain, spinal cord, and sacrum. Disrupting this rhythm puts pressure on the cranial bones and other parts of the body, leading to neurological dysfunctions and other maladies.[3])

Possible side effects of craniosacral therapy, the therapist told me, include heightened emotions in the days following a session. After his first session, Chris reported hearing New Age music—and he knew that no music was playing in the room. My treatment was pleasant and relaxing. (I didn't hear any music.) Chris had three sessions over the course of three weeks, and nothing in his behavior seemed out of the ordinary during that time.

Just before leaving on our vacation, Chris attended a five-day workshop organized by the choir director of our church. The training included group and individual voice coaching and incorporated exercises from the Alexander Technique, a discipline that is familiar to many musicians, dancers, and actors, as well as people seeking relief from back pain.[4]

Practitioners of the technique learn to adjust unconscious physical and mental habits and to reprogram their responses to stress. I'd recently read that Kitty Merrick Wielopolska, who trained in the technique in the 1930s, credited her eventual recovery from schizophrenia to diligent adherence to the exercises.

F. M. Alexander was an Australian actor who suffered from chronic laryngitis. Failing to find relief from medical doctors, he began to study his body position for clues about the origins of his condition. The process took him years.

Alexander started with the premise that the way he held his neck was creating a strain on his voice. He thought he could relieve pressure on his neck by moving his head forward and up, away from his body to lengthen his spine. When the problem persisted, he realized that, rather than focusing on specific movements, he needed to look at the way he was moving his whole body. He concluded that he couldn't trust his senses; he'd thought he was moving correctly, but often he was not.

Body habits die hard, Alexander found, and try as he did to correct faulty movement patterns (a tendency he referred to as bodily "misuse"[5]), he would habitually revert to them. Eventually, he realized that these patterns originated in his subconscious mind. If he wanted to change them, he must first find a method for becoming consciously aware of them.

Alexander's approach to self-examination required consciously stopping the movement pattern he was executing to decide whether he wanted to continue it, change it, or stop it altogether and do something different. The technique he developed seemed like an approach that Chris could use to address the "action–no action" dilemma he frequently encountered in relation to using both his mind and his body. He might finally learn how to *choose*.

However, I had also read that use of the technique could trigger the release of suppressed feelings and emotions. (Craniosacral therapy can have a similar effect.) I hoped that any risks would be outweighed by the benefits. Chris was really enthusiastic about what he'd learned of the Alexander Technique during the voice training workshop. I hadn't seen him so fully engaged in an activity in a long time.

Shortly after the workshop ended, our family flew to North America to begin our vacation. Taylor and Alex stayed with friends in the Washington, D.C. area while Ian and I drove Chris to his scheduled college visit.

Touring the campus, Chris asked relevant questions of the staff members in a friendly, relaxed manner. He was invited to come back later that day for a small get-together of students and staff, which he happily attended. His academic future was showing some promise.

The following morning, we drove back to D.C. and picked up Taylor and Alex. Next, we all headed to the Maryland coast, where we had rented a beach house for a week, an opportunity for our family to be together before a new school year began. Taylor and Alex would both be staying in the U.S., and this would be our last family get-together for a while.

But something wasn't right. Chris was becoming distracted and a bit standoffish. He was also walking very, very slowly, like a blind man feeling his way.

My heart sank a little lower every day. I had seen this behavior before. These were the first signs that Chris was beginning to slip back into psychosis.

Chapter 34

Psychosis Again? ✴

WE WERE ON a tight schedule. Alex was returning to Indiana to resume his studies at Purdue; Chris would fly to Newark and take a connecting flight to Geneva. Dwelling on my fears was not an option. Psychosis or no psychosis, when our beach vacation was over, we headed for Dulles Airport.

Ian, Taylor, Chris, and I bid farewell to Alex at the security checkpoint and then walked to another part of the terminal to find Chris's departure gate.

Concerned that something might go wrong during Chris's travels, Ian grilled him about his preparedness.

"Have you got your passport?"

"Yes."

"Boarding pass?"

"Yes."

"Money and phone?"

"Yes."

"Okay. When you get through security, go straight to your gate. Don't dawdle."

The three of us watched as Chris went through the screening process. We waited until he turned and waved to us and then got back into our rental car and drove the two hundred miles to State College, Pennsylvania so that Taylor could begin his orientation week.

Ian and I planned to spend a bit of time touring Virginia and North Carolina after we helped Taylor get settled into his dorm. We were traveling through Virginia when Ian's phone rang. Fearing the worst, he pulled over to the side of the road before answering the call.

"Hello?"

An anxious voice said, "I missed the flight to Geneva."

"Why am I not surprised? Where are you now?"

"Newark. I spent the night in the airport lounge"

"And how did this happen?" Ian asked, irritated.

"Well, I started talking to this biologist while I was sitting in the lounge waiting for my flight. He was really interesting, and the next thing I knew, they had closed the gate. When I realized that the gate was closed, I ran up to the glass door and started pounding on it."

"Chris! You're lucky you weren't arrested. You don't do that sort of thing post-9/11. People will think you're a terrorist!"

"Well, they almost did. Anyway, I'm really sorry about this. I've got a seat on a plane to Geneva today."

My husband's tone softened as he sighed and said, "All right. These things happen. Just make sure you get home in one piece."

Ian and I looked at each other. Worrying about Chris was unavoidable; he was likely to continue to need our oversight and financial support for some time to come. We enjoyed the rest of our vacation in spite of the intrusion of reality into our plans for Chris to pursue an academic degree at a school in the U.S.

Our household was much quieter that fall without Taylor around. I had hoped that taking courses at Webster would occupy Chris and help fill the void. After a couple of weeks, however, it became apparent that he was not keeping up with his assignments. School was not a priority for him, and he was becoming more and more distracted.

I talked to him at length about the change I was witnessing. I couldn't understand why he was so disoriented. He'd been well before we went on vacation.

He confided that his perceptions were changing. At choir rehearsals, he said, he was vocally out of sync with the other members.

"You hear that police siren?" he asked me.

I paused to listen and heard the faint sound of a siren off in the distance.

"Now it seems like it's just a siren, but before I used to think about all the bad things that must have happened to someone or the crime that had been committed. I'm still stuck halfway between the old perception and the new one, and I get disoriented sometimes. My experience of physical reality is changing. It's like I don't know where to look or put my feet."

I could have framed these confessions in a negative way and reacted with alarm, but I chose to believe that Chris's use of the Alexander Technique and the sessions he'd had with the craniosacral therapist were having the desired effect: his perceptions were returning to normal.

Normalcy, however, can seem disappointing to someone who is accustomed to living in a fantasy world. One evening, I found Chris lingering outside our apartment building, looking sad.

"Did you keep your appointment with Doctor Stern?" I asked.

"I stopped on the bridge and couldn't go any further. I just held onto the railing. It seemed so far away."

I fought the panic that was beginning to stir inside me. I had never worried much about Chris being suicidal, but I sensed that he had been drawing closer to reality in the past few weeks. Other people might think he was drawing away from reality, but what I saw was a person who was experiencing loss. This transition can be perilous.

I decided to inquire further about the nature of my son's despair. "It seemed so far away" could refer to several things—the Rhône River that boiled below the bridge, Doctor Stern's office, the railing itself. Or was he referring to the distance between where he was in life and where he wanted to be?

"Why don't you come upstairs with me?" I suggested gently. "I'll fix you something to eat, and we can chat."

Back in our apartment, I cooked a minute steak and made a small salad for Chris. He barely ate anything, pushing the salad around on the plate with his fork. His eyes reddened as he told me that, earlier that day, he had gone into a store to pick up an item Taylor had asked him to get.

"When I walked in, I realized the store was not *my* store. It was just a store." He started to cry.

Seeing him suffer was painful, but I reasoned that he was beginning to see the world as it is, a necessary step to functioning in it.

"And then what happened?" I asked.

"I walked along the street, where the trams are, and then I had a coffee." Chris continued to weep. "What have I done, Mom? What have I done? I am not God!"

Chris's candid confession that he was not omnipotent and omniscient needed careful handling.

"You may not be all-powerful and all-knowing, Chris, but you have a divine spark within you, as we all do."

I had a hunch about Chris's insight, but I wasn't certain I was right, so I probed for more information.

"What is the hardest thing for you to imagine right now, Chris?"

After a pause he said, "Is this all I can expect?"

"Did someone say something to you today?" I asked.

"Yes, several people did."

Rather than play Twenty Questions, I offered a suggestion.

"Chris, is it possible that you are beginning to perceive a new reality, and it doesn't seem as exciting to you as your fantasies?"

"It's so . . . It's so . . . It's so . . ." He wiped his eyes.

"Boring?" I ventured.

"What have I done?" he lamented. "What have I been doing?"

"You know, reality, as most people perceive it, can be exciting too," I said. "You should give it a try!"

Chris looked up from the table and managed to laugh before shedding more tears. "I'm so sorry, Mom, for everything I put everyone through."

"What do you mean? Your crisis, in an odd way, has been beneficial for all of us. We've had to band together and look out for one another, and we've become closer as a result. We should *thank you* for being the catalyst!"

I encouraged Chris to go to his room and lie down, and I draped a blanket over him. I turned off the lights and pulled a chair close to his bed.

"I miss Taylor," he said.

"I miss him, too," I said, taking his hand in mine.

He grasped my hand with warmth and gratitude, and I felt like a good mother to him for the first time in a long while. I sat by his bed while great sobs shook his body.

"Just cry it out, Chris, for as long as it takes."

After a few moments had passed, I said, "Fantasies are fine, in their place. Don't lose your creativity, because that is precious. God wants us to make the most of the life He has given us. We honor Him in this way by succeeding in life on earth. You are on the verge of fulfilling the potential that God has given you. Now, cry some more and then go to sleep."

If only talking and crying were enough to cure what ailed him.

Chapter 35

❋ More Twists in the Road

AS I THOUGHT MORE about Chris's disclosures, I imagined that there could be several explanations for his latest behavior. In his book *In Search of Stones*, psychiatrist M. Scott Peck, MD writes that one of the great principles in psychiatry is that all symptoms are "overdetermined," meaning they have more than one cause.[1] Doctor Peck believed this idea was so important, it could apply to almost anything that a person considered significant—not just to psychiatric symptoms.

I wondered if the changes in Chris that I was witnessing resulted from the craniosacral therapy and/or the Alexander Technique. (Chris had been practicing the Alexander Technique on his own, at home, on a daily basis since attending the voice workshop four months earlier.) His heightened emotions could have been precipitated by Taylor's departure, especially since Ian and I were encouraging him to leave home, too, and go far away to college.

Maybe he's panicking, I thought. *Maybe he's afraid of being on his own.*

Another possible explanation was that his feelings and emotions were no longer being blunted by medications.

Doctor Erika suggested that even though Chris had been off the medication for almost eight months, he could still be experiencing the effects of withdrawal. Her long-distance muscle testing indicated that Chris's dopamine levels were elevated and he needed something to help calm him. She recommended the amino acid L-tryptophan, important for the production of both serotonin and vitamin B_3.

Whatever the causes of Chris's recent behavior, I was hopeful that the changes signaled growth. In other areas of his life—the organized parts, such as attending classes and showing up on time for appointments—he was definitely regressing.

Other people were also wondering what was happening to Chris. Instead of directly asking him what was going on, they asked me. "Oh, he's just going through a rough patch," I'd say.

What looks like relapse may sometimes be part of the recovery, I kept telling myself. Without that conviction, I might have lost all hope.

Ian and I insisted that Chris drop his two courses at Webster rather than risk failing them. He didn't need a lot of convincing. He knew he was on shaky ground. He continued to show up late for his choir practices and eventually stopped going altogether. He was too disengaged to follow instructions from his voice teacher, so his private sessions stopped, too.

Upon learning that he was giving money to gypsies, I started to think that maybe we should give him a weekly allowance rather than a monthly sum. (I'd hoped the knowledge that his parents trusted him to manage his money would encourage him to spend it wisely, but that was when he was in better control of himself.) The amounts he was giving away were trivial, so I opted to continue the monthly allowance.

Then I received an e-mail from Doctor Stern. Though we all had agreed at our quarterly meeting, barely two weeks earlier, that Chris probably didn't need medication, she was now strongly recommending that he go back on both a major tranquilizer and an antidepressant. She was worried that he might be suicidal.

I approached Chris about Doctor Stern's e-mail and learned that he had relayed the wrong message to her about something I had said. (I'd never said anything suggesting I thought he was suicidal.)

"Chris, there are at least two things you can tell a psychiatrist that are guaranteed to have them pulling out the prescription pad. One is admitting that you're hearing voices. The other is mentioning suicide in any context, even jokingly."

Doctor Stern was doing what any psychiatrist would have done under the circumstances. Once the S-word has been spoken, psychiatrists must take the threat seriously. Nonetheless, I was very disappointed and somewhat angry with her. Ian and I had engaged her specifically to help get Chris off the medications. Now, in addition to my other worries, I carried the odor of fear around on my clothing. Nothing could wash it out. My fear was that I could be wrong—and Doctor Stern could be right. *Chris could be suicidal.*

However, I was concerned that if Chris went back on medications, his recovery would be postponed—possibly forever.

I sat down with him at our dining room table. "What you decide to do about the medication is up to you," I told him. I avoided trotting out the reasons why I was against them; Chris knew them well.

"I'm afraid that if I go back on the medications, I'll never be able to function at Webster," he said.

I knew he wasn't functioning at Webster now, having dropped his courses, but the medications could, in my opinion, make his academic prospects worse in the long run. I said nothing, however.

Chris decided to send an e-mail to Doctor Stern, which he copied to Doctor Erika, Ian, and me, reassuring her that suicide was the last thing on his mind. He was sorry if he had confused her, he said. He wasn't against the medications, he just didn't believe they were right for him.

"My feeling," he wrote, "is that I am the cause of my own depression, but I hope that it will lift just as the clouds melt away after a summer thunderstorm."

Chris, always willing to blame himself, may have been telling Doctor Stern what he thought I wanted him to say. And on this subject, he would have been right.

Later, I sent Doctor Stern an e-mail informing her that I had deliberately stayed out of Chris's decision about the medication, largely because I was tired of parenting him and believed he needed to learn to make his own decisions. I assured her that in the unlikely event that Chris killed himself, I would consider the decision, and the responsibility, to be his—not mine, not hers, and not Doctor Erika's.

I added that, should Chris choose to go back on the meds, I refused to monitor his pill intake. The chances were high that, without supervision, he would be noncompliant—with disastrous results—but I was not willing to go down the medication road again, and I was tired of doing his thinking for him.

For the time being, the matter was closed.

Chapter 36

❋ A Multifaceted Approach

CHRIS HAD ESCAPED going back on medication, but his symptoms still needed to be addressed. He could see a psychotherapist for years (possibly without really recovering), or we could explore other approaches that might help him find and maintain a sense of well-being.

Remembering how readily Chris had come alive during our play readings, I reasoned that he might benefit from further study of the Alexander Technique. He had enjoyed learning the basics, so why not encourage him to learn more?

Chris was hesitant about contacting Laurel, the teacher from the voice workshop, for private sessions. He told me he was wary of creating further perceptual changes.

Unthinkingly, I blundered and asked him if he considered himself handicapped. The question caught him by surprise.

"Uh, no, not really," he said. "Why?"

"I don't think you're handicapped, either, but sometimes you *act* handicapped, so other people may *perceive* you as handicapped. Your nervousness makes other people nervous."

Ever since he was a toddler, Chris's entrance into a room had been remarkably quiet. (He would leave a room as silently and mysteriously as he entered.) While this appearing-and-disappearing act was noticeable when he was small, as an adult, the behavior became bothersome. Chris would hover by the doorway and, eventually (either of his own volition or after being asked by an irritated family member to either come in or go away but stop loitering!), he would inch his way into the room. Once inside, he would pause, walk a bit, pause some more, and then reverse direction.

Attempts to sit down were painful both for Chris and for anyone watching. He would bend his knees and sway a bit, as if positioning himself to sit, and then he would hesitate and stand back up. I thought the Alexander Technique could help him learn to move more intentionally, with greater ease and less awkwardness. (Actors, after all, must consider the impressions created by their movements.) I was confident that Chris was capable of learning how to successfully sit down in a chair!

In retrospect, I wish I hadn't told him that he appeared handicapped, even if I went on to say that I did not believe he was. People do best when given positive feedback. (I could, instead, have simply pointed out to Chris that he'd done well using the Alexander Technique and might benefit from private sessions with Laurel.)

Fortunately, he followed my suggestion, despite the clumsy way I presented it. He returned from his first forty-five minute session with Laurel a different person. Over the course of the following week, he was less hesitant in his movements. He threw off the gloom that had been dogging him for years and seemed more lighthearted. He rejoined the choir and signed up for another course at Webster. Then, as quickly as these new developments had surfaced, they vanished.

Coming home from work each day, I worried about what I would find when I reached our apartment. Sometimes, Chris seemed more or less together; at other times, he'd be staring off into space. Some days, he would only speak to Ian or me while standing in another room. I noticed that his speaking voice was lower but shrugged off this weird new development as one of the effects of the Alexander

Technique and probably a good thing, in the long run, thinking that a lower-toned voice signals confidence.

Chris soon entered a more manic phase. He spoke in a great rush of words and interrupted Ian and me with emphatic but off-base observations. I could only imagine what his classroom performance at Webster was like and feared he would have to drop yet another course. After discovering that he had blown his monthly allowance in one week, I began to dole it out to him in smaller amounts. "Bipolar Chris" was a new development.

Doctor Erika called, announcing, "I have it! I think I can explain why Chris has been having problems recently."

She had told us to stop the amino acid L-tryptophan a couple of months earlier, believing that Chris no longer needed it. She had since learned, however, that L-tryptophan is needed to bring elevated dopamine levels down to a normal range.

Ian and I endured two more weeks of Chris's erratic behavior before the L-tryptophan arrived in the mail. The change in Chris after only a few days of taking it was astonishing. The mania was gone, and he was able to sit and converse with us—while in the same room.

Once again, I was reminded of the importance of getting the biochemistry right. (Techniques to help Chris function better in social settings would be of little use if he was manic or psychotic!)

I knew better than to think that biochemistry alone was the answer. The mainstream approach (i.e., pharmaceutical interventions) had not proven effective in my son's case, and if I'd believed that Chris's problems simply required correcting biochemical imbalances, then I might have overlooked the role of psychospiritual distress as a causative factor. But if I had relied exclusively on unconventional explanations for his condition, I might have ignored new scientific findings about the causes and treatment of mental illness.

Mindful of M. Scott Peck's assertion that symptoms can have multiple causes, I abandoned my naïve expectation of solving the mysteries of schizophrenia. (Where had it come from? Why was it still here? How could I make it go away?)

I was learning to accept my limitations as caregiver. My willingness to try anything, within reason, was wearing me down. How long could I continue as nurse, therapist, vitamin dispenser, and all-around mom before I collapsed?

My day of reckoning was just around the corner.

Chapter 37

✳ *Do-It-Yourself Soteria*

DESPITE THE UPS AND DOWNS Chris had been experiencing for several months, I still believed that continued use of the supplements (combined with therapy sessions with Doctor Stern twice a week—and my loving care) would be enough to keep him out of the hospital.

I was wrong.

I was also exhausted. Ever since Chris had started following Doctor Erika's program, my routine had been pretty much the same. I prepared Chris's supplements on Sunday for the week ahead. Pill organizers could no longer contain all the pills and capsules Chris was taking, so, instead, I made my own paper packets and labeled them with a number (1, 2, or 3), depending upon whether they needed to be taken with breakfast, lunch, or dinner—twenty-one packets each week. I boiled two liters of water every evening, and in the morning I mixed in powdered and liquid supplements. Chris drank this stinky green concoction throughout the day without complaint.

He seemed determined to throw Ian and me off guard. I realized he was harboring deep anger toward us, but, rather than openly confronting us, he took an indirect route. He gave more money to gypsies and made a point of telling us what he'd done, knowing we'd be angry. He hinted that he was falling behind in his coursework, hoping, I suspect, to arouse our fear that he would be unable to keep up with assignments. Ignoring these provocations wasn't easy, but Ian and I agreed that giving the expected response would only encourage more of the same behavior.

I wanted off this damned roller-coaster ride. I hated being home alone with Chris. He was making no useful contribution to our household—no intelligible conversation, no job, no prospects—and now he was depressed and angry. I became angry and depressed myself. Chris's rebellion, if that's what it was (and not a symptom of disease), had come late, but I clung to the notion that this developmental stage was a necessary one.

Ian and I had several frank talks with Chris about his attitude. Not surprisingly, he was often apologetic—but on one occasion, he blurted out, "I hate you both," as if he was revealing some awful secret.

"We can live with that," we chorused, "but *you* are having trouble living with your deep-seated anger, and it is getting in the way of your moving on. You are only harming yourself. You don't want to move on at this point, do you? Because you are scared of growing up and taking responsibility for your life. You'd rather blame us."

The only way to avoid these scenes was by staying out of the apartment as much as possible. For the sake of our own sanity, we had to stop micromanaging Chris's life.

When we were at home, we tried to ignore Chris's many peculiarities. We severely cut back on the number of guests we entertained because we didn't want to expose others to the pall that was cast over the household.

By December 2008, Chris was experiencing serious mental turmoil, reminiscent of the period before he left for Toronto six years earlier. He was slipping further into psychosis, and this time I watched it knowing full well what was in store.

How could I have let the situation go this far? How could he have lost so much control over his impulses?

I was glad that he was becoming more emotionally expressive, but he was also becoming seriously unglued—losing his keys and his Swiss identification card, not showing up for appointments, singing loudly in the streets, and jumping and twirling around the apartment. One time, I had to dissuade him from parading through the streets of Geneva, on his way to church, dressed in his bright-blue choir robe.

He was also spending inordinate amounts of time in the bathroom, and, even so, he was urinating in his pants. More ominously, I found traces of fecal matter on the walls of the bathroom and on the parquet floors.

Doctor Erika discovered from talking with Chris that he had stopped applying the footpads she had prescribed for him months earlier to help his body detox after the medications had been withdrawn. (Chris was supposed to put these pads on his feet every night before going to bed.)

According to Doctor Erika, Chris was in a state of toxic buildup, which contributed to the expression of anger, mania, and depression that Ian and I were witnessing. Whatever the cause of his current state, we needed to find a way to fix it—and fast.

Christmas that year was hell. Chris was behaving in his particular psychotic way, crouching on the floor, speaking only the most banal thoughts laced with hints of aggression, taking long pauses before answering simple questions. He continued to urinate in his pants and to decorate the apartment with small flecks of feces.

Alex and Taylor were back from university and none too happily sharing a bedroom. They barely spoke to Chris. He irritated them. This pained me tremendously, but I understood why they reacted the way they did. Chris irritated *me*. My anger and criticism toward him had given his brothers tacit permission to treat him badly.

One morning I woke up around 4:00 a.m. to find Chris standing in the darkened hallway. He wasn't sure if he was awake or asleep. I gently led him back to bed.

Before she left on vacation, Doctor Erika e-mailed an updated list of products for Chris to use (including creams to support his liver during the detox process and Epsom salts for baths)—a last-ditch effort to help him get through this crisis.

Unlike Doctor Stern, Doctor Erika was not in favor of putting Chris back on a major tranquilizer. Reluctantly, she recommended a mood stabilizer to help keep his symptoms in check.

Ian and I liked the idea, reasoning that withdrawing from a mood stabilizer after a short course of treatment would be easier than getting off a neuroleptic. Doctor Stern agreed that a mood stabilizer might work and prescribed a small amount of valproate sodium.

Administering the mood stabilizer once a day was easy compared to dispensing all the supplements Chris was taking. (Doctor Erika had recently added sublingual drops of lithium and sulphur to Chris's regimen.) Twice a day, I slathered the detox cream over Chris's liver and dabbed a special niacin cream that is supposed to work wonders with psychosis on his temples and wrists and behind his knees. I made sure he was putting on the detox footpads every night and taking a bath with Epsom salts every two days.

Fantasies of sending Chris to a mental hospital so I could be relieved of my round-the-clock caregiver duties entered my mind on a daily basis, but I knew that he would be given a neuroleptic drug immediately upon admission, and maintaining his supplement routine while he was hospitalized would have been difficult, if not impossible.

I also was acutely aware that Chris would assume the role of a mentally ill patient if he was in the hospital. The irony wasn't lost on me that he had taken on the same identity at home, and I was playing nurse. He wasn't bedridden, but he might as well have been. He was that helpless.

Providing a nurturing environment may have been the key to success in programs like Soteria, but, without training and without a support staff, my attempts to replicate the Soteria model at home fell short. My husband and I had full-time jobs and our own lives to live.

I was reaching a new low. The only positive conclusion I could draw about Chris's condition was that he must surely be moving up the ladder of diagnostic labels. When it comes to stigma, a thought disorder (such as schizophrenia) is on the lowest rung. Moving up to what seemed more like a mood disorder (such as bipolar) was a strange sort of progress, but Chris's anger, hostility, and tearful outbursts seemed preferable to an apathetic, ambivalent Chris.

He was, at least, more alive!

Chapter 38

Back in the Bin ✳

ON NEW YEAR'S DAY 2009, Chris and I braved the icy paths and took a walk in the park across the street from our apartment building.

As the sun sank lower in the sky, we plunked ourselves down on a bench. After enduring several months of tension, we had little to say to one another.

"What do you see when you look around you?" Chris asked.

"Reality, Chris," I said, exasperated. "I see reality."

"I see the Atlantic Ocean," he said, gazing in the direction of the sunset.

"Come on, Chris, the Atlantic Ocean?"

"Okay, I see the Rhône then," he said, glancing to the south.

What was he talking about? The Rhône River was not visible from where we were sitting. I changed the subject. Trying to understand my son's thought process held little appeal for me these days.

We reminisced about life in Ottawa during his childhood. Chris talked about our neighborhood and his school.

I decided to go further back. "Chris, do you remember anything about your time in utero? You must have liked it because you spent ten months there."

Suddenly animated, he nodded and said "Oh, yes!" with the now-familiar glazed look of psychosis.

My interest aroused, I said, "Really? Tell me what you remember."

"Well, it was kind of gooey and red. Apart from being completely aware that I was in the cell, and hearing the guitar that Dad played, it was nice because I felt really close to God during that time. I haven't felt that close since."

"So why did you decide to venture forth at all, after ten months?"

"I felt I had to see if there was more to this life."

"And what have you found?"

"I see God and feel His presence, but not as completely. He's there in that tree and in the air. Knowing He's there covers the pain."

I refrained from asking him about the nature of his pain; that would have to wait for another day. We were getting cold. It was time to go inside.

Through the month of January, Chris fluctuated between barely functional and not-at-all-okay, but the clear trend was downward—for me, too. Worry prevented me from getting a good night's sleep, and I now hated the supplements almost as much as I hated the medications. Every supplement that Doctor Erika recommended (in addition to the recently introduced mood stabilizer) was supposed to be absolutely necessary to prevent the decline in Chris's mental state—which was occurring nonetheless.

Toward the end of the month, we ran out of niacin cream and had to wait a week for it to arrive by mail. I prayed the cream would arrive before Chris went completely bonkers. The people who had marveled at how well he was doing without medication were now urging me to put him back on it.

Reluctantly, Ian and I asked Doctor Erika to recommend a neuroleptic. (Doctor Stern had agreed to prescribe whatever drugs Doctor Erika recommended.) While we waited for the cream and Doctor Erika's answer, I asked for guidance from the Higher Self.

I recalled a story I'd read about one of Doctor Hoffer's patients, a young man who would swallow a whole bottle of niacinamide capsules when he felt he was going over the edge. (Hoffer recommended up to six grams of niacinamide a day for his patients, with an equal amount of vitamin C (to prevent possible liver damage) and a B complex (which helped increase the effectiveness of the niacinamide).)

Chris was taking two grams of niacinamide per day, so I doubled his dose and gave him four grams. (I also added the requisite amounts of B and C vitamins.) Within twenty-four hours, I observed dramatic results. After dinner, Chris sat down at the piano and played some traditional Scottish tunes by ear. (He hadn't touched the piano in months.) The following day, I took the afternoon off work and came home to find him chuckling over some *Seinfeld* episodes. (He hadn't laughed in months.)

Over the next few days, Chris ate his dinner faster and seemed much less agitated than I had seen him in a long time. The tension between us began to ease.

Nonetheless, I was doubtful that the pronounced changes I observed would continue. Chris had been taking niacinamide in varying quantities for several years, and he always responded well to it, in my opinion, yet here he was, psychotic again. His participation in the HOPE program hadn't prevented relapse, nor had two weekly therapy sessions with Doctor Stern. I didn't know how to stop a florid psychotic episode, other than with drugs, and we were running out of options.

Clearly annoyed with Ian's and my inability to prevent Chris's deterioration, Doctor Erika recommended Abilify. (In her opinion, one atypical neuroleptic was no better or worse than another. In other words, there was nothing special about her choice of Abilify to treat Chris's particular symptoms.) She maintained that the supplements, if properly administered, could prevent the need for hospitalization, and her pointed e-mails documented her position

If the decision had been mine alone, I would have been willing to wait a few days before filling the prescription, to see if Chris would rebound from the psychosis with the continued use of the niacinamide formula. But Ian was unwilling to wait any longer. (At least Doctor Stern would be relieved, I thought, and we could tell all those well-meaning people who were concerned about Chris that, yes, he was back on medication.)

Chris was taking 5 mg of Abilify for less than a week when he unraveled further.

I'd gone to London for a couple of days, so Ian decided to take Chris to Germany for a change of scenery. They had a wonderful time, during which Chris was symptom-free, according to Ian. We all returned home on Saturday evening.

Sunday morning, Chris got up early to attend choir practice before the church service. (This behavior was remarkable in itself, as rehearsal was usually well underway before Chris showed up.) When Ian and I arrived at church an hour later, Chris was in the office. (The rector told me later that when the choir director suggested to Chris that he open the hymnal, he snapped at her and said there was no reason why he should. At some point, Chris punched a fellow choir member in the arm. He was becoming mildly aggressive, and the rector had suggested that he stay put in the office until Ian or I came to get him.) By the time I found him, he was distraught and hallucinating. ("I think I may have bent a lamppost on the way to church, but I'm not sure.")

The next day, Ian and I took Chris to the clinic connected with the HOPE program. We brought along an overnight bag that included Chris's toiletries, a change of clothes, and packets of supplements. We had discussed a possible overnight stay with Doctor Stern several weeks earlier, and she'd promised to get in touch with the clinic to alert them that Chris might be coming in.

We were wrong about the clinic's services, however. The facility did have beds for overnight observation, but respite care was not on the menu. (The two intake psychiatrists we spoke with said they had no record of Doctor Stern contacting them.) In retrospect, I believe that Doctor Stern knew exactly what would happen if we showed up at the clinic with Chris in the condition he was in: the doctors there would send him to the hospital.

When the discussion with the psychiatrists turned to hospitalization and commitment, Chris became quite talkative and managed to resurrect his French language skills, which had been dormant for several months. His paranoia was evident. "I don't like you much," he told the dark-skinned psychiatrist.

"Well, given that you don't even know me, what exactly is it that you don't like about me?" the man asked knowingly.

Chris glowered and turned away.

The psychiatrist filled out a pink form, ticking all the boxes needed for commitment: "danger to himself and others," "obvious symptoms," and "not able to be accommodated elsewhere." With a satisfied grin, he handed the form to Chris. I hadn't noticed until then that a burly attendant had quietly slipped into the room.

When Chris realized what was happening, he jumped up and lunged at Ian. "You bastard!" he yelled.

The doctors rose up to restrain him, and the newcomer jabbed him with a needle.

I was oddly encouraged by the skirmish I was witnessing. By verbally expressing his rage toward a parent, Chris was no longer being a "good little boy." His open anger seemed like progress.

Chris was given two anti-anxiety pills (in addition to the tranquilizer that had been injected), packed into an ambulance, and transported to Belle-Idée.

Mentally, he was in much better shape than the two other times he had been hospitalized. He had a developed some resiliency. And he was angry.

Chapter 39

✳ *Time and Space*

CHRIS ENTERED BELLE-IDEE with a one-week supply of supplements. (I prepared my usual 1-2-3 packets of pills and capsules for Chris to take throughout the day. Emil Blancpain, MD, the head of the unit, agreed to have the nursing staff administer them at the appropriate times. The liquids I delivered myself.)

"I have such hate," Chris said glumly when I visited him a few days later.

I was glad he'd admitted it, but I said nothing.

When I stopped by the nursing station after our visit, I was informed that other patients were avoiding Chris and making fun of him because he was soiling his pants. Doctor Blancpain had ordered suspension of the vitamins for a couple of days to see if the problem would correct itself. I suggested to the pretty young nurse that maybe Chris soiling his pants was a sign of anger or depression and not the result of taking vitamins.

For heaven's sake, I thought, *we're in a psychiatric hospital. Let's see shit for what it most likely is in this case—the unloading of pent-up anger.*

I wasn't willing to entrust Chris's health to the whims of the hospital staff, so, thereafter, I visited the hospital daily to bring Chris his vitamins, and I sat there while he took them. (I left some packets in the closet for him to take when I wasn't there.)

Three weeks after Chris's admission to Belle-Idée, Doctor Blancpain met with Ian and me for the first time. Looking up from his file he announced, "Chris's incontinence problem has cleared up, so the decision to suspend the vitamin supplements was the correct one."

"Doctor Blancpain," I politely interjected, "I'm sorry to poke holes in your theory, but Chris has been taking the supplements all along. The vitamins have nothing to do with Chris's incontinence. My guess is that anger does."

Doctor Blancpain's face flushed, and he quickly regained his composure. "Well, then, under the circumstances, Chris may as well continue to take his supplements," he said.

I smiled at him, content that he'd grudgingly accepted the reality of the supplements, even if he didn't see the value of them. The doctor paused slightly before asking, "Tell me, Monsieur and Madame Forbes, to what, then, do you attribute Chris's improvement?"

"That's easy," Ian said. "He's away from *us*!"

"It was getting absolutely awful at home," I agreed. "Chris was angry, and the situation just kept getting worse. Now that he's away from us, and we're away from him, he's had a chance to reflect and calm down."

"I see," said Doctor Blancpain. "Well, providing space for time out is something we do well here."

Ian and I laughed, but this simple answer, time and space, was perhaps the thing Chris most needed at this time. Doctor Blancpain, however, trained in the language of Pharmaceutica, was determined to get us to agree to increase Chris's dose of Abilify. He also wanted to add a new major tranquilizer.

"We find that two low-dose neuroleptics taken concurrently are almost always more effective than using only one," he said.

"I don't agree," I said. "Chris has been on two medications before. I don't see two drugs as any more effective than one. And, personally,

I don't think people should be taking these drugs at all. There's got to be a better way."

"Madame Forbes, the research shows that people need to continue on low doses of neuroleptics for a long time and not go off them."

I knew that some mental health professionals were questioning the wisdom of using brain-altering drugs for long periods of time.[1] I'd brought an excerpt from a journal article (the results of a fifteen-year longitudinal study) to the meeting with Doctor Blancpain. I handed it to him before Ian and I left and urged him to read it.

The study, by Martin Harrow, PhD and Thomas Jobe, MD, identified a subgroup of schizophrenia patients who did not immediately relapse when they stopped taking antipsychotic drugs.[2] These individuals experienced intervals of recovery, suggesting that not everyone who is diagnosed with schizophrenia will need to use medications continuously and indefinitely.[3]

Despite my steadfast efforts to wean Chris off all medications through the judicious use of supplements and alternative therapies, he ended up back on two drugs (Abilify and Serdolect) during his stay at Belle-Idée. I got tired of being the odd one out. I had no more energy left to fight. If Ian or Chris had joined me in opposing the medications, Doctor Blancpain might have backed down. Ian, at this point, was Strongly in Favor of keeping Chris on a neuroleptic—for life, if necessary. He didn't want, ever again, to endure anything resembling our experience over the past six months. Chris, for his part, didn't seem to care one way or the other.

I wasn't planning to start a new battle on the medication front, at least not for the time being. (Doctor Stern had stated all along that she saw medication as a short-term solution—a position that conflicted with Doctor Blancpain's practice of keeping his patients on two neuroleptics for long periods of time.)

Our relationship with Doctor Erika, the holistic psychiatrist, ended the moment we put Chris in the hospital. She no longer wanted him as her patient.

"If he had faithfully followed my treatment, this couldn't have happened" was the gist of her complaint and, presumably, her way of documenting her position in case we filed a lawsuit. (She needn't have worried. Ian and I had no intention of filing any complaints against her or Doctor Stern. They were both trying their best, in accordance with their respective approaches to treatment—treatments we had wanted to try.)

Chris was discharged in May 2009 after three months at Belle-Idée. To my dismay, one of the first things he did when he came home was dig out his old set of fantasy cards that he'd had since he was ten years old. I wondered if the hospital stay had helped him at all. (Chris's interest in the cards continued for another year; at that point, he donated them to a thrift store. "I think they're too young for me," he said.)

Doctor Blancpain assigned two young doctors connected with the HOPE program to monitor Chris's medications for a year following his discharge from Belle-Idée. Ian and I met with the doctors (with Chris present) once a month to share our impressions of Chris's progress and to raise any concerns. One of my concerns was that Chris had gained back all the weight he'd lost when he wasn't taking any drugs. (Another new set of clothing!)

I kept my mouth shut, but my silence couldn't continue forever. At our final meeting, in April 2010, I stated my objection to keeping Chris on two medications. I was completely unprepared for the response I got.

"We agree with you!" said one of the doctors. "The latest research shows that one medication is better than two!"

The doctor was probably referring to the research findings ("the more drugs you've been given, the more brain tissue you lose"[4]) of Nancy C. Andreasen, MD, PhD. Science was finally backing up what I'd been saying all along. (Score one for mother!)

Chris's Serdolect was phased out in favor of Abilify only.

Now, with at least some sanity restored to our lives, I could focus on helping Chris with what I believed he needed most: finding a way to move forward.

Chapter 40

※ Hearing and Listening

"Mozart," I thought, and with the word conjured up the most beloved and the most exalted picture that my inner life contained.
— Hermann Hesse, *Steppenwolf*

WHILE CHRIS WAS HOSPITALIZED at Belle-Idée, I started researching the Tomatis Method, a "listening reeducation" program developed by French physician and otolaryngologist Alfred Tomatis (1920–2001).

The "Tomatis Effect," recognized by the French Academy of Medicine in 1957, refers to the proposition that the voice can only reproduce what the ear can hear.[1] In other words, if an individual is unable to hear certain frequencies of sound, those frequencies will be absent from his voice as well.

Doctor Tomatis distinguished *listening* from *hearing*. Whereas hearing is passive, listening is an active process. Listening ability allows us to focus, which has profound implications for spatial awareness and control of bodily movements.[2] (Listening is important for "most skills involved in communication, verbal as well as non-verbal, socialization, language and learning."[3]) The ear charges the brain and nervous system with electrical energy, and its proper functioning is essential to motor skills, balance and coordination, and, of course, hearing.

In the womb, the fetus hears predominantly high-frequency sounds[4] and is nurtured by the mother's voice.[5] Tomatis suspected that many childhood learning disabilities and emotional disorders develop because the fetus had been unable to hear certain frequencies, impeding proper development in utero.[6] Through his research, he concluded that the best way to activate the brain and increase attentiveness and learning ability is by exercising the muscles of the inner ear. To help his patients achieve optimal hearing (and, therefore, learning), he invented the "Electronic Ear," a device that recreates the sound environment of the womb by alternating high- and low-frequency sound ranges using filtered recordings of Mozart music,[7] waltzes, Gregorian chants, and the human voice.[8]

While searching for a Tomatis program nearby, I discovered that a psychologist friend had recently started working at a center in Rolle, a town northeast of Geneva.

Marsha told me Doctor Tomatis had placed great emphasis on the psychological aspect of hearing. He developed an audio-psycho-phonological (listening) test to assess a person's listening potential and determine whether audio-vocal reeducation was needed.

I learned that the refusal to hear creates pressure in the middle ear, which results in the inaccurate perception and analysis of sound by the brain. (Schizophrenic individuals tend to hear mostly higher frequency sounds, Marsha said.) Reeducating the ear can help people by better anchoring them in their bodies through correct hearing and auditory processing of the lower frequencies.

Satisfied that Chris would benefit from the Tomatis Method, I took him to the Rolle center in May 2009, soon after his discharge from Belle-Idée.

The center's *directrice* showed us around. Our tour started outside, in the gardens. Next, we moved inside, where children and adults lounged in chairs or sat at tables doing artwork while wearing headsets.

"Participants are encouraged to spend time drawing or painting," the directrice told us. We followed her up the stairs to see the language booths that are used in the later stages of the program.

Chris's listening ability was evaluated by a staff member, and I was given a form to fill out. As Chris's mother, I was invited to respond to questions about my pregnancy, the labor and delivery process, and whether Chris's development was unusual in any way.

The questionnaire was no place to be coy. I filled entire pages, and then some. I wrote about my forty-four week pregnancy, the fall on the pavement, the fact that Chris barely moved in utero, the twenty-four hour labor, the lack of breast milk, my arguments with Ian during and after my pregnancy, our financial worries at the time, Chris's claim that he'd seen space aliens in the park at the age of ten, and so on.

Chris and I met with the directrice to go over the results of Chris's assessment. He was not properly hearing some sound frequencies, we learned. (Medications can decrease the accuracy of the results, we were told.) In the reeducation program, Chris would come to hear his voice in a new way.

"Using both bone and air conduction to hear and listen is crucial for the development of a self," the directrice said. "You will hear your true voice for the first time."

Chris started the program the following week. For thirty-one days, I drove him to the center before I went to work. (He took the train back to Geneva when he was finished for the day.)

I was extremely encouraged by the subtle changes I observed during this time. Chris's voice changed in a way that I could not define; it sounded deeper and more resonant. He spoke more with his brothers about factual, day-to-day things (and less about philosophical ramblings or poetic flights of fancy). His body movements were a bit more fluid. He seemed calmer and more determined. He told me his dreams were more vivid and continuous.

All of this signaled to me that he was becoming more grounded. I believed that as long as we stayed the course, his difficulties over the past six years would soon be behind him. He was beginning to live less in his mind and more in his senses, as he explains in his remarks about his experience in the Tomatis program:

Chris's Self-Assessment of the Tomatis Method

If you've ever seen *A Clockwork Orange,* based on the novel by Anthony Burgess, you can perhaps better appreciate the idea behind the Tomatis Method. In the film, violent Alex loves Beethoven, but after undergoing rehabilitation, including hearing his beloved Beethoven played over a Nazi propaganda film, he is "cured" of his love of violence but also of his love for Beethoven. By filtering and repeating, *ad nauseam,* Mozart and Gregorian chants, you begin to question all your senses and how you derive pleasure from them. The Tomatis Method is really maddening and you get the urge to run somewhere away from the music, and you start to blame yourself a bit for the pain of the constant repetition. It gets lonely as well, with no one to compare your art with and no one to think about while you're listening to the music.

I have always been a fairly primitive visual artist, yet I've found an appreciation for everything that goes into painting something with meaning. In my Tomatis sessions, I mostly drew stick figures and simple landscapes, little outdoor scenes with some children or a stormy afternoon. For an eleven-year-old, it wasn't bad, especially the ones where I used crayons. I really want to paint or draw well, but now I notice how every little effect of color, the texture of the crayon or paintbrush, becomes so important to me that I know I can't draw what's in my mind because my senses are controlling me.

It's difficult to describe the effects of this particular therapy because of other therapies and techniques I have undergone. I didn't hear Mozart ringing in my ears as I did my food shopping, but I did become a little tired after the session was over and just wanted to watch TV and relax, anything to "center" me so I could feel alert to confront the rest of the day. There were overlaps with the Alexander Technique, craniosacral therapy, gem therapy (assemblage point shift), and, indeed, dear old singing lessons. With singing, one of the most important things to get right is being in tune, and I have known people who cannot sing when the rest of the choir is out of tune with respect to the piano. I've noticed that I've become more exacting from my voice, that it is more difficult to sing out of tune. So everyone else is singing, and all of a sudden, I stop completely. How much of this can be attributed to overconfidence I'm not sure.

I have noticed that after the therapy I felt much more communicative, and exposed. Previously, when I became angry with my brother over a television show or something similarly stupid, I was able to control my emotions and articulate my frustration. Now, with this heightened emotional sense, I find that when I listen to people, they aren't just "a body in space" anymore, but I hear the subtext of their concerns; their emotional presence makes them "people."

The Gregorian chant from the sessions really makes you pay attention to the "spiritual presence," and this is both confusing (people are less predictable) and also exciting. I get the sense that people can float in and out of rooms, and I start to lose my sense of self. Also, I became more critical of myself, noticing every change in breathing or of not being comfortable and this was very annoying. The music totally clears your head, so you can't fixate on any one idea or topic, you have to put aside any concern you presently have, because you're in another place altogether.

Chris's positive response to the Tomatis Method, and to music in general, inspired me to look for other forms of sound healing. Several months later, I learned of a talk by a man who uses sound frequencies to increase life force energy. Accompanied by my husband, I sat in the front row—and listened.

Chapter 41

✳ *The Sound Shaman*

PIER RUBESA addressed the audience that had assembled at a pastoral retreat center north of Lausanne, Switzerland one Sunday morning in the fall of 2009. He spoke about his background and how he became interested in the effects of sound waves on plants and animals. A sound engineer, composer, and musician, he had been profoundly impacted by several near death experiences.

This man must surely be a shaman, I thought.

Shamans, I knew, act as bridges between the human world and the spirit world. By entering different states of consciousness (whether through trance or out-of-body experiences) they access information that can help bring harmony and healing to individuals and their communities.

Quoting from the Book of John, Rubesa equated the Bible's reference to the Word of God[1] with the Big Bang,[2] which, he speculated, occurred at a frequency that approximates the color red, long associated with the root chakra of the human energy field.

He gestured to a computer and other electronic equipment that sat atop a table at the center of the stage. "The sound you are about to hear is produced by my invention, the Bioscope system, and is the frequency of the color red," he said as he flipped a switch on one of the components.

A low, rumbling sound emanated through speakers positioned in the corners of the room. After several minutes, I was shifting uncomfortably in my seat. Mercifully, the sound stopped before I felt compelled to run for the nearest exit.

"The energy released in the Big Bang continues to imbue human beings, plants, and animals with a unique harmonic resonance or life force," Rubesa said. "Exposure to sound waves and electromagnetic fields affects us in various ways—some positive, some negative. We may sometimes require rebalancing to stay healthy."

The frequencies produced by the Bioscope match the colors that are thought to correspond to the chakras of the human energy field, Rubesa said. As I listened to the next sound, I recalled that proper functioning of the chakras is essential to maintaining good health.

"The Bioscope is designed to detect and analyze the subject's life force energy both before and after the application of sounds like the ones you just heard," Rubesa said after the sound stopped. He explained the meaning of the graphs that were now displayed on a screen behind him.

"Much of my research has been focused on agricultural produce. The graph on the left represents the scan of a tomato that has been treated with pesticides. The one on the right is of an organically grown tomato. Notice the difference in the structure of the electrical fields surrounding each tomato. The chemically-treated tomato has disruptions in its field, whereas the field of the organic tomato is more coherent."

The marked difference between the two graphs sold me on the importance of consuming organically-grown produce.

"This next pair of graphs shows the same tomatoes after they've been exposed to frequencies selected to enhance their life force."

Though I didn't fully understand what the graphs were measuring, I could see a significant difference in the "before" and "after" slides. The chemically-treated tomato now looked nearly as healthy as the one that was grown organically.

When Rubesa paused to invite questions, I raised my hand and asked if he treats specific illnesses or conditions.

"I'm still in the early stages of documenting the effects of the Bioscope on people," Rubesa said. "I'm not a medical doctor. I don't hold out the promise of cure, and, no, my method does not address specific conditions, so I don't want to know what people's health concerns are when they come to see me."

I e-mailed Pier Rubesa a few days later to book appointments for both Chris and me.

I understood that his work was experimental, but I thought his approach held great promise as a means of helping balance and harmonize Chris's energy system. (His physical energy was too low, and his mental energy too high.)

By experiencing the therapy myself, I hoped to further my holistic healing research and, perhaps, correct any underlying health problems before they manifested as illness.

I wasn't expecting any miracles. If the Bioscope could help in even subtle, positive ways, I'd be grateful.

Chapter 42

Colorful Sounds ✳

ON A GOLDEN AFTERNOON in early October 2009, Chris and I arrived at Pier Rubesa's village in the Canton of Fribourg. We followed the directions he had given us but couldn't find his house. I phoned his office number but got no response.

Chris and I were both frustrated. Overheated from the journey and getting on each other's nerves, we were about to give up and go home when the shaman drove up in his car. He led us through the village and up a steep road no wider than a cow path.

Rubesa's home and office was a weathered chalet that had been built in 1602 (according to the date carved over the door). Standing on the rickety balcony, I heard the distant sound of cowbells.

"Follow me—and watch your head," Pier said.

The three of us walked down a dark hallway with a low ceiling to a central room that was surprisingly airy and spacious. The sweeping view of the valley below was breathtaking. The chimes outside the open window tinkled in the breeze, and I detected the faint aroma of burning wood.

"I do most of my work in here," Pier told us.

Ah, the bed is for clients, then, I thought, looking around. Chunks of quartz crystal and a statue of the Buddha gave the room a mystical feel.

"Chris," the sound shaman said, "I know that your mother heard my talk a few weeks ago, so she is somewhat familiar with what I do. When you have your session, I'll explain the therapy in more detail. For now, let me introduce you to my equipment."

We walked over to a table, where a laptop computer and other electronic equipment were set up.

"This is my Bioscope system," the inventor said. "These wires connect to electromagnetic sensors that are located under the bed's mattress and also to the speakers that you see in the corners of the room."

He sat down at the table and opened a file on his computer. "While you are lying on the bed, the Bioscope will send carefully mixed sound frequencies through the speakers. These frequencies of the visible light spectrum correspond to the vibratory colors of the seven major chakras. The primary importance of the chakras is thought to be in the psyche, but they have a secondary physical importance, too," he explained. "Your body emits electrical currents in response to these frequencies, and these responses are detected by the sensors in the mattress. Based on how you respond, I vary the frequencies to help you attain greater balance, both physiologically and psychologically."

Pier promised to show us graphs of the measured responses at the end of the session. "Any questions before we get started?" he asked.

"None yet," said Chris.

"Your mother has the first appointment, so feel free to take a book from my shelf and go out on the balcony while the sun is still out."

Chris glanced through Pier's books and pulled out a copy of Joseph Campbell's *The Hero with a Thousand Faces* before disappearing down the hallway.

Lying on the bed, I closed my eyes and tried to relax while Pier tested the audio levels. Occasionally, he got up from his table and walked across the room to reposition a speaker.

"Okay, all systems are go," he announced. "As I introduce each sound, I will tell you which color we are hearing. I want you to visualize that color and keep visualizing it for as long as the sound lasts. I will establish a base reading and determine where you are energetically weak. We can compare this baseline to future readings to see where you are improving."

"Sounds good," I said. "Which color do we start with?"

"Red, the color associated with the root chakra, which is located at the bottom of the spine. Broadly speaking, the root chakra governs the survival instinct—fight or flight—and the adrenal glands."

"Red" began for me like the low, sawing sound of a bow on a double bass. It soon became something different, more like the ground-shaking vibration of an immense primordial creature, thundering in intensity as it got closer to where I lay, curiously unafraid, in its tracks.

After a few minutes, the frequency shifted to a slightly higher sound as the color orange was introduced. Orange, Pier said, is associated with sensuality, strength, and the reproductive organs. Yellow, green, blue, indigo, and violet, the highest of the frequencies transmitted, followed.

After about twenty minutes, Pier said, "This next part will give your vital force a boost."

A mixture of sounds began, swirling around and through me with increasing intensity. I felt wonderfully relaxed, as if meditation had suddenly been made easy. For twenty minutes, I let the sound do the work.

When it was over, I rested for a few minutes before opening my eyes.

Pier explained the possible changes that I might notice over the next few days. Fatigue and tiredness, and aches and pains in places where I may have had an operation or an injury, were the notable ones.

Next, Pier showed me the "before" and "after" scans of my energy field. (The "before" scan was the base reading Pier made of each of the colors; the "after" scan was done during the twenty-minute mixture of sounds.)

"Overall, you are in excellent shape," Pier said. (The phrase "for someone my age" remained unspoken, but implied.) "You have demonstrably improved in the orange life-energy field."

I peered at the graph.

"Well, yes, my 'after' energy for the orange does look more robust compared to the 'before,'" I commented.

Orange is about confidence and sociability—exactly where I was in need of a boost. So much of my energy in the past few years had been directed inward, reflecting on my choices and shortcomings, as well as searching for ways I could help Chris. I'd had little time or energy for making new social contacts.

Chris's session was next. I wandered out onto the balcony and picked up the Joseph Campbell book Chris had left there. Settling into a chair, I rested my feet on the railing and enjoyed the last remnants of daylight before the sun dipped behind the mountains. Eventually, Chris joined me there, and we said our goodbyes to Pier.

On the drive home, Chris and I compared notes. His physical response to his first sound therapy session seemed unremarkable. His next few sessions, however, would be transformative.

Chapter 43

Lucid Dreams *

I HAD A TOTAL of three sessions with Pier Rubesa. I found the Bioscope experience pleasant, for the most part. My response to each sound-color was different, though I perceived most of them as calming.

Green was the exception. Something about the green vibration made me want to jump out of my skin, so uncomfortable was the sensation. Green is the color of love and the heart chakra; it's the color of spiritual growth and renewal and symbolic of life's interconnectedness. When I was listening to the "green" sound, I didn't care what the color represented—I just wanted the sound to stop.

As much as I might have liked to drift into an altered state, I wasn't able to surrender and let go. Chris, on the other hand, was able to let go with relative ease. During his second session, he had the first of many out-of-body experiences. I asked him to keep a journal of these experiences, which occurred regularly during the year he was having Bioscope sessions with Pier (2009–2010). Here is what he wrote after his second session. (He was initially bothered by flies in the room.)

I began to fall into a trance, an aware sort of sleep; instead of relaxing into my body and dreaming, I left my body and begun [sic] to experience the room while my body "powered down." First I said to myself, this is just a sound, a basic unrefined sound but just a noise really, and then my head refused to make any noise, any comment or utter any "thoughts" as I was released into the space or "aura" around me.

I could see my body lying down from four feet away in any direction, and it was the best impression or image of myself that I've found in a long time, better than any mirror image can give. Those flies that I found so irritating I now realized were in harmony with my feelings of irritability that I had carried in with me, and I could fly around the room as if the flies were part of me. The only pain I felt was at the head level, when I could see that a big dark block at my head masked or obstructed this free flow of energy I experienced. To stand up in that state would have been impossible.

The following morning, Chris had a lucid dream[1] about the television show *The Simpsons*:

I had been thinking about skiing the night before, and in this dream the Simpson family went skiing high up in the mountains, and Bart and Lisa got involved in the dangers and thrills of racing and jumping. When I felt scared at the outcome, and the dangers posed to the characters were too great, the story changed, based on my emotions. I suddenly realized I had the power to create a dream and change it based on my emotions!

The next day, Chris reported seeing a woman wearing white. She entered his bedroom while he was reading and tapped him on the shoulder. "I could feel her touch," he wrote, "but I realized it was still a dream. My head was telling me to get off the bed and do something else, and here was this woman who appeared also compelling me to get up."

I'd learned the hard way to keep my own counsel about Chris's kooky-sounding experiences, because the doctors at HOPE had routinely rejected my suggestions if they competed with the program's accepted approach (Doctor Erika's vitamin supplements being a prime example). Unfortunately, my son had not yet learned this lesson. When Chris, Ian, and I met with Doctor Stern a few days after Chris's first out-of-body experience, at our quarterly meeting at the end of 2009, Ian spoke about Chris's good progress, and how pleased we both were that he was working with an occupational therapist (OT) recommended by Doctor Stern.

Doctor Stern was glad to hear this and offered a few observations of her own, based on three years of regular therapy sessions with Chris. Then, pausing briefly to signal a change in topic, she leaned forward in her chair.

"What's this about Chris having an out-of-body experience?" she asked. "His OT told me about it. She also said something about a lucid dream and a lady in white tapping Chris on the shoulder. I'm concerned he might be hallucinating again."

I glanced at Chris to gauge his reaction. He seemed relaxed. I, however, was fuming inwardly and wishing he could read my thoughts: *Chris, do you want to end up back at Belle-Idée?*

I took a deep breath and told Doctor Stern that I believed Chris's sound therapy sessions were helping to ground him. "The incident he's referring to occurred in a therapeutic setting and under controlled circumstances. Mister Rubesa spent a lot of time with Chris, explaining what might happen during the session, and, later, what did happen and why Chris reacted the way he did. Chris has had lots of lucid dreams, but now he's beginning to see that these dreams may be the products of his own emotions. He's developed a clearer sense that he's not crazy, and he's learned that he can control the outcomes. Many people try to develop their capacity to experience lucid dreams; it's something that comes naturally to Chris. I don't see that as a cause for concern."

Doctor Stern folded her arms and frowned, unconvinced.

"Do you practice yoga, Doctor Stern?" I asked. "Occasionally, yoga can also lead to out-of-body experiences, but sometimes yoga is encouraged for schizophrenia patients."

"Well, I wouldn't want Chris having an out-of-body experience in a yoga program, either," she said. "Chris should aim to be *in* his body, not floating outside of it."

The news about Chris's out-of-body experience and the lady-in-white incident came as a surprise to Ian, who, thankfully, didn't interject with, "Let's put a stop to all this nonsense now!"

I was praying for the session to end. I didn't want to have to explain myself to both Ian and Doctor Stern. Doctor Stern had been open-minded enough to work with Doctor Erika, but there was no point trying to sell her on out-of-body experiences for Chris, so I simply said, "I understand your concerns, and if I were you, I would feel the same way. I will think more about what you said, and I'll share some information about the sound therapy with you."

Before our meeting ended, I excused myself to make a phone call from Doctor Stern's inner office. I noticed a large quartz crystal on a table near the door.

Did Doctor Stern know about the healing power of gemstones and vibrations or was the crystal just a decorative object? I wondered. Or was I looking too hard for meaning in ordinary objects and events? *Sometimes a rock is just a rock.*

Chris later told me that the rock was actually a clock.

I was surely going mad.

I never got around to sending Doctor Stern information about Pier Rubesa and his Bioscope, and she never inquired further into Chris's therapy—or out-of-body experiences.

Neither did Ian.

Chapter 44

Broken ✳

WORKING WITH PIER over the next year, Chris felt that he was able to understand his emotions better and started to question whether he'd been living too much in his head.

> As I heard the colors and shapes, I could see that my "mind" had been tricking me, or rather my body was wanting to make my mind believe that my feelings were my body, and were somehow inferior to the form of a beast that I had allowed my body to become.

He attributed the changes he was experiencing, in part, to the ability of the color-sounds to bypass his conscious mind ("the sounds reaching all my cells without interference from my mind").

> I am humbled to say I feel as if I have no control whatsoever of the images and thoughts that come to me as I lie down at the therapy. If there is any improvement in my well-being as a result of the therapy, well it is hard to say what part I played in it.

Pier suggested to Chris that his mind, with its endless stream of chatter, is not the real Chris. As he developed the ability to detach from his thoughts, Chris started to see that his thoughts are not his true self.

> When the sounds began, I felt I could live inside my body with so much space, every nerve and muscle vibrated with the sounds, so that my leg felt like a wooden bat and stretched as long as the ceiling is high. My mind, usually relegated to my head and stuffed into his tiny cubicle, opened the windows on all my body and became clearer and louder.

He also speculated about the reasons for his inability to find a career path or vocation.

> I believe that when I've chosen to follow an abstract goal, committing intellectually, emotionally, and physically but without a true purpose, then a split was caused in my being, which is why I haven't been able to find a true calling yet.

In one of their final sessions, Pier told Chris about the rites of passage followed in some tribal cultures and planted the idea of a vision quest.

> He then asked me to imagine I was entering a desert from which I could not return as I came, and posited I may find someone or something there, bringing a message.

Chris wrote about his experience as follows:

> I saw a cactus, but it was enormous, filling up my field of view, and I couldn't get past unless I let it prick me. Once I felt the pain, then the view opened up and I could see for a mile around. There was nothing remarkable until I began to imagine myself thirsty and was surrounded by the cactus once again.

As I lay on the ground, my vision shifted to that of an eagle, or bird-man, and as he flew towards me we became one animal, and I felt held up high by a strange force, and at last I started to fall towards the earth because my right wing was broken. I noticed that right before the sounds stopped, I was ignoring the broken wing and was happy just to be able to fly. This must show how I needed something extra to return home from the desert, the awareness that I was not fully healed; the feeling of being lost before finding my wings is the same as the insecurity of flying with a broken wing. Having no wings and crashing with a broken wing amount to the same thing from the perspective of being on the ground; if I can't fix my wing I stay on the ground, but if I want to fix it and fly I have to give up roaming the desert.

After his sessions with the sound shaman ended, Chris was wiser, but not necessarily happier. At twenty-six, he was still living at home, and, though stable, he was unable to work or study. He needed to find a meaningful way to fill his days.

Chapter 45

✳ *Building Rapport*

"I'D LIKE TO TAKE more care with how I do things and how I look," Chris said as he stirred a pot of fish stew. (He'd bought the ingredients after finding a recipe in one of my cookbooks. The result was a steaming bowl of whitefish, clams, and colorful peppers in a spicy red broth. It tasted delicious.)

Chris's declaration cheered me, because in the past he hadn't seemed to care what he ate (peas or carrots) or what he wore. He was starting to become interested in taste and color—and the outer world.

"I began to first think something was seriously wrong with Chris," my husband once said, "when he chose the dullest gray tie imaginable from a rack of real beauties." (Ian is a tie person.)

"That's otherwise known as 'flat affect,' dear," I responded. "Chris needs more zest. It doesn't come naturally for him."

By the time Chris was in his mid-twenties, I'd developed several coping strategies. I continued reframing my observations to stay positive about Chris's recovery. In addition, I would occasionally imitate some of his behaviors, a technique that I later learned is called "mirroring" and is used as a rapport-building exercise in therapy.

I found Chris's ghostlike presence unsettling, so I decided to try being ghostlike myself. Upon arriving home, I slid my key as silently as possible into the lock, opened the door, and stepped lightly over the threshold, taking care to oh-so-silently shut the door behind me so that nobody would know I was there. (If I could have slipped in through the keyhole like a "real" ghost, I would have.)

I glided past Chris without acknowledging his presence and quietly busied myself with whatever tasks I needed to do. I tried hard not to rattle the dishes as I put them away, and I spoke loudly enough to not appear conspicuous but quietly enough to achieve the desired effect.

My efforts seemed to make an impression on Chris. On several occasions, he tapped lightly on the door of my bedroom, where I had deliberately holed up to avoid him. When I didn't immediately respond, he opened the door to check on me, asking "Is there anything I can do for you, Mom?"

"No, nothing at all," I murmured as I continued my reading. "Please shut the door behind you when you leave."

The hoped-for results were not long in coming. I would hear Chris's key turn firmly in the lock and then, "Mom, I'm home!" *Bang, bang, bang* went the pots and pans.

I didn't have the staying power to continue mirroring Chris for more than a few days, but I didn't need to. After about a week had gone by, Chris's ethereal nature no longer bothered me as much. Whether his ghostlike behavior truly became less pronounced, or through my little experiment I had stepped into the ghost's shoes and emerged changed, I cannot say. Perhaps we'd both changed enough to interact with greater ease. In any case, the rapport-building exercise was a success.

Chris had not been at Belle-Idée in nearly two years, so his request to go there to talk to a psychiatrist seemed to come from out of the blue. He'd been depressed for about a week, and I was worried about him. I phoned home from work one afternoon to check on him.

"I'm so lonely," he said. "I'm so lonely."

"What can I do to help?" I asked. "Is there anyone besides me you'd like to talk to?"

"I want to go to Belle-Idée to talk to a psychiatrist," he said.

I didn't inquire further. (Apparently, any psychiatrist would do.) I told my boss that I was taking the rest of the day off and drove home to get Chris and take him to Belle-Idée.

I waited in the parking area until Chris joined me, about an hour later, looking happier and more relaxed.

"The doctor says there's no need to admit me, but I am welcome to come back any time and talk to him."

I was never more thankful to Belle-Idée than I was then. That wonderful doctor had acknowledged Chris's loneliness and had spoken to him like a friend.

Chris never did go back to talk with the psychiatrist, but finding suitable companions took some time. His vulnerability and his generous nature made him a magnet for Geneva's mentally unstable and its *colporteurs* (hucksters) and *mendients* (beggars).

Chris was in his late twenties when his social life began to pick up a bit. He took more voice lessons and recommitted to the church choir. He started volunteering at the local soup kitchen and for a citywide food collection depot. Occasionally, he helped performance artist and friend Fredie Beckmans[1] construct birdhouses.

Venturing further afield, Chris joined the men's chorus of the local amateur operatic society, composed of English-speaking expats. The group stages a variety of productions each year—Gilbert and Sullivan shows, Broadway musicals, Christmas pantomimes. (Tim Berners-Lee, inventor of the World Wide Web, was once an active member.)

Chris had managed to create a busy social life for himself. He performed solo several times with the church choir, and he was fitting in nicely with his chosen communities, despite his continued challenges in social settings.

I was delighted to see how busy he was, but his schedule was lopsided. Though his nights and weekends were full, his days were still empty.

Chapter 46

Finding a Life Path ✳

> You may yourself as an artist develop the game of your life and lend
> it animation. You may complicate and enrich it as you please. It lies
> in your hands.
>
> — Hermann Hesse, *Steppenwolf*

LONG STRETCHES OF TIME passed, during which Chris did
almost nothing during the day except run an occasional errand for his
parents. He met twice a week with Doctor Stern (for psychotherapy),
once a month with the occupational therapist, and once a week with
the church choir director (for voice lessons).

I was sometimes annoyed with Doctor Stern's calm acceptance
of Chris's slow progress. I had complained to her a few years earlier,
when Chris was twenty-four years old and I thought he should be
back at university, but she dismissed my concern as premature.

"He's only twenty-four," she said. "He has plenty of time."

Now Chris was twenty-seven, and I saw the window of opportunity
for him to become skilled and independent beginning to close.

I wondered whether the occupational therapy was accomplishing anything. Chris had been working with this OT, at Doctor Stern's suggestion, since he left Belle-Idée, but he was nowhere near ready to resume his education or hold a steady job. How long could he continue to pass his days with no productive work, no reason to get up in the morning?

He approached me one day with an assignment the OT had given him. "Mom, I'm working on a résumé that I want to show to a vocational counselor downtown. Can you help me with it?"

He handed me his one-page draft, which he'd typed on the computer, in French. In addition to the year he'd completed at the University of Toronto, Chris noted that he'd taken "a couple of courses" at Webster. He also noted that he "likes playing the guitar and singing."

I knew that Chris's hobbies would not land him a paying job (which, presumably, was the point, although no objective was stated on the résumé). Any employer would wonder, "What were you doing the rest of the time?"

The assignment revealed Chris's deficiencies—and I felt pretty sure that both the OT and Chris recognized the problem, too. Still, this first step, getting Chris to think about employment, was an important one. The counselor he was scheduled to see routinely worked with clients referred by the OT, so I viewed the exercise as a starting point.

"I can help you a bit with the French," I told Chris. "I can also think of some activities that you can add."

He took his revised résumé to the meeting with the counselor the following week. His stricken face when he came home afterward told me that something had gone seriously wrong.

"We talked about suicide," said Chris.

"Suicide? You're joking, aren't you?"

"The counselor was very nice, but as we got talking I started to cry, and she gave me some tissues and suggested that maybe I wasn't yet ready for work. She asked if I needed any help getting home, but I said no."

I didn't take the suicide talk seriously; Chris doesn't understand the perils of sharing his inner life outside of the therapist's office. I was upset, however, that he'd blown an opportunity to find employment. A job—any job, at this stage—would have filled his days and given him a new social outlet.

Skilled by now at reframing my fears, I concluded: *Chris is afraid of becoming independent, which is understandable. Perhaps he'd rather kill his chances than take a job he'd hate. He's an ARTIST! Cut him some slack! Focus, instead, on helping him find a way to earn money doing something he enjoys.*

A few months later, when I could laugh about Chris's interview, I said to him: "Look, you might never work in an office because, well, that's not what you're about. I think you've been on your career path all along and you just don't fully appreciate it. Let's rewrite your résumé with Sue Frederick as our inspiration."

I had recently given Chris the book *I See Your Dream Job*, in which career intuitive Sue Frederick uses numerology and astrology to steer people toward the career paths they are best suited for. Based on the Pythagorean idea that each number carries a cosmic vibration, Frederick's book provides a simple formula for calculating the number that represents our "life path." By combining the life path number with the astrological sun sign, a person's unique type can be determined. When we understand our type, we can make choices that are consistent with our innate strengths and talents.

In this system, Chris is a Capricorn 3. Number 3 is creative; acting, music, and writing are listed as possible career paths that would allow Chris to put his talents to good use. Unlike the hardworking Number 4 (Chris's mother), who often get lost in the drudgery, Number 3 needs to enjoy what he is doing or he will quickly lose interest.

The description confirmed what I knew to be true about Chris but, thus far, he hadn't been able to see.

"You *are* creative, Chris," I told him. "You are a musician. You're elegant and playful. But Sue Frederick says that the negative qualities of your type will predominate if you are not doing what you love to do. You can be overly intellectual and unwilling to face up to your responsibilities."

I had recently started pushing Chris to think of music as a career focus, not merely a hobby, so the book confirmed my belief that a job in the entertainment field would be a good fit for him. Using a musician's résumé that I found online as a guide, I rewrote Chris's résumé and added his volunteer work. I included details about his performances (titles and venues)—but no dates.

Chris's makeover was spectacular, a veritable tour de force. His activities now filled an entire page; he didn't need to reveal that his experience had all been acquired in the past two years. At the top of the page, under his name, he announced himself as a vocalist, a guitarist, and a community volunteer. The revised résumé showed him what he was capable of doing, and it helped him believe in himself. That belief is what will carry him through.

For someone who had spent the better part of ten years in a fog of self-doubt, fantasy, loneliness, and inertia, knowing his type gave Chris reassurance that he was on the right track, and the mystical component of Sue Frederick's system appealed to him.

I hadn't fully appreciated, until I was writing this book, that Sue Frederick's message also applied to me. I'm not the creative type, but I enjoy persistent, repetitive work, being efficient and logical, and I have the ability to wring simple out of complex. I wish I had known about the unique attributes of my number when I was young. I could have learned to appreciate and cultivate my strengths. I'd wobbled all over the place, job-wise, only grasping fairly late in life that I could have had a satisfying career (in a factory maybe?!) if I'd been better able to capitalize on my innate talents.

Chris still had time to establish himself as an artist, if that was the direction his path was taking him. His life took on new meaning and focus when he added meditation to his daily routine. "Reaching Nirvana, Do Not Disturb" said the sign posted on his closed door as he learned to let the noise in his head fade away.

Or, at least, he learned to turn down the volume.

Chapter 47

✳ *Bionergetics*

BY THE AGE OF TWENTY-EIGHT, Chris was much more animated in the way he expressed himself, but sustained social interaction was difficult for him. Years of psychotherapy had given him insights about himself—and others—but he still had trouble expressing his thoughts clearly, and he often digressed down pathways that were hard to follow.

His desire to be of service was also a hindrance to social interactions. He assumed that people wanted help, which wasn't always the case. He crossed my boundaries on a regular basis. When my patience reached its limits, I admonished him.

"You are sapping your energy and focus by putting the well-being of others ahead of your own needs. If people want your help, they'll ask. And that includes your father and me! We're not doddering old folks yet. Concentrate on your own life. We can take care of ourselves."

Chris and I needed to start distancing ourselves from each other. We'd had an intense ten years. Maybe we needed to take a break from alternative therapies and let nature take its course, I thought.

Alas, Nature must have abhorred the vacuum created when we talked about giving our holistic excursions a rest. Within a year, two new opportunities popped up. To get a sense of Chris's interest in trying them, I broached the subject of further resiliency training.

"You've read Joseph Campbell, Chris. Which of his quotes is most memorable?"

"Something like, 'the mystic swims with delight in the same waters the schizophrenic is drowning in.'"

"Everything we've tried up until now has been aimed at keeping our heads above water. Think of these approaches as swimming lessons or resiliency training. Are you interested in doing more?"

"Sure, why not?"

For our first stop, we went to see Jean-Pierre, a biologist who claimed he could extract the energy from plants for therapeutic uses. "Diagnoses don't interest me," he told me when I called to arrange an appointment. "Just bring the results of a recent blood test." I complied and brought test results for Chris and me, though the reason Jean-Pierre wanted them wasn't clear.

Despite his brusque manner on the phone, Jean-Pierre was actually a jolly fellow. "Don't confuse me with a homeopath," he told Chris and me when we arrived at his house on the outskirts of Geneva. "I'm simply a nature-loving Frenchman who studies the effects of the resonance energy of plants on the human body's endocrine system."

Jean-Pierre introduced us to his assistant, Severine, who sat behind a computer at one end of a long desk while he circled and bobbed his way around the room, checking his equipment and refilling his hummingbird feeder before settling down next to Severine.

Using muscle-testing, Jean-Pierre determined which of his numbered vials, containing different plant essences, Chris reacted to.

"I'm searching for the energies that weaken you," he told Chris.

When he found them, he called out the numbers on the vials and Severine entered them into the computer.

"The computer analyzes the information and lists the plant essences that will improve your health and vitality. While we are waiting for the results, I will hook you up to my bioenergetic equipment to see which organs and related systems may be under stress."

Jean-Pierre asked Chris to remove his shoes and socks and stand on two brass plates on the floor. Severine fastened a brass band around Chris's head and handed him two brass poles, one for each hand.

"We are going to measure the electrical conductivity of different parts of Chris's body," Jean-Pierre said. "This device can detect illnesses and disease patterns before any physical problems would be apparent through conventional testing. I use the results to validate my muscle testing. On your next visit, we'll check to see if the potions I give you today have been effective."

Chris was given several potions to take home. When we returned a few weeks later, I sat in the waiting room, engrossed in a Jack Reacher novel, while Chris was retested. I got up to stretch my legs and was looking at a jar of the honey that Jean-Pierre, a beekeeper, had for sale when Chris emerged from the treatment room.

"I have no immune system," he told me.

"How strange," I said, putting down the jar. "You're never sick."

"He said my immune system is so bad, it could be in the Guinness Book of World Records. But he says these potions will fix me."

Indeed, four months later, Jean-Pierre declared that Chris's immune system was now functioning normally.

Had Chris's immune system really changed? I can't say for certain, but I did notice that, subsequently, Chris would suffer from occasional cold or flu symptoms. I view these minor illnesses as a positive sign. If Chris's immune system is functioning properly, maybe his mental health will improve as well.

Jean-Pierre had no idea that Chris had been diagnosed with schizophrenia, but his testing detected something amiss that conventional doctors had overlooked.[1]

He tested me several times and found that I was in good health, in general. When the occasional sniffle or sore throat was detected, I came home with some plant potions to boost the functioning of my immune system.

During the time that Chris and I were taking Jean-Pierre's plant potions, we were also working with George, an engineer friend whose company develops and sells products that shield the user from "e-smog"—electromagnetic radiation emitted by electrical power systems, computers, cell phones and the like. These products can be worn on the body or be used in a home, office, or vehicle.

George also offers sessions for correcting a person's electromagnetic fields. He first measures the fields using a device that connects to a computer. (The fields appear as colors of the visible light spectrum.) The computer program includes a database of the electromagnetic frequencies of healthy cells, organs, and systems. By scanning a person's photo into the computer, George can compare the individual's frequencies to normal standards. If deviations and abnormalities are found, they can then be corrected.

George told me that indications of trauma can be detected before any physical (or psychological) manifestations have developed; even ancestral patterns and traumas that occurred to other family members can appear in a person's fields.

If his program could really do all that he claimed it could, I was game to find out more. Putting aside my inner skeptic, I sent him a recent photo of Chris and arranged for a session.

George came to our apartment one morning and explained the functioning of the radionics system he uses. If the results of the photo scan show a lot of imbalances, he said, he uses a computer program to clear the unresolved traumas. When there are only a few, as was the case with Chris, he uses color cards.

George placed a plastic-coated 8 ½ x 11 inch card and a battery-operated light on the table. Color therapy, he told Chris and me, is based on resonance.

"Each person has a unique overall frequency, or Key, as well as frequencies that are associated with cells, organs, and systems. All of these frequencies can be seen as colors. The computer determines which of the person's frequencies are out of balance. In Chris's case, nothing in his Key indicates a state of chronic stress, which tells me that he's been able to handle traumatic events relatively well."

I asked George how he defines trauma.

"When we experience stress—whether from an illness or an event—our equilibrium is thrown out of balance. If an individual has developed adequate coping mechanisms, his immune system will handle short-term stresses and acute injuries, but if a trauma remains unresolved, the immune system is compromised. The source of the problem often lies in the unconscious."

George's computer program detected periods of Chris's life when he might have experienced a trauma that was still affecting him adversely. The color therapy cards would be used to ascertain when the traumas occurred, George explained. Unconscious blocks could then be cleared.

The color card that George placed in front of Chris was selected based on Chris's Key. A multicolored band in the center of the card was bordered by a timeline, which was divided into groups of years (e.g., ages 5–8, 9–12, and so on) that corresponded to childhood and adolescence. George instructed Chris to place a finger in the blank area of the card while George moved his index finger along the band.

"I want you to visualize what was happening in your life in each of these time periods," he told Chris.

When George detected resistance at a particular spot on the timeline, he stopped.

"We'll change Chris's cellular vibration at each resistance point by having him place his hand on the light," he said. "That creates equilibrium and restores cellular energy."

"Hold on," I said. "How does putting his hand on a light clear unconscious resistance from his past?"

"It's a special kind of light," George said. "It's got a microcrystal-line resonator embedded in it that helps remove negative energies."

The exercise would be repeated until all points of resistance were cleared.

I asked if the lack of resistance meant that underlying problems were completely gone.

"Getting at someone's problems is like peeling the layers of an onion. Our traumas are often hidden. You clear some things up and then older problems come to the surface, but usually not immediately. We'll repeat the exercise after a few days or a few weeks, perhaps with different cards, and clear whatever resistance is found. Usually, only two or three sessions are needed."

I went to another part of the apartment to give Chris and George some privacy. When I returned, less than an hour later, George was preparing to leave. Chris had disappeared into his room.

"I wondered about Chris's early teen years," George told me, "and I think there could be something going on, but Chris couldn't recall anything distressing that happened during that time period. I'd like to repeat the therapy in about a month."

After Chris's next session, George warned me that Chris might pull away from me because a point of resistance had been cleared. He didn't explain further, but for several days I felt sad, intuitively knowing that something had changed irrevocably. Even if the change was for the better, I felt a sense of loss.

The following weekend, Ian and I attended a performance of the operatic society Chris was part of. When the concert was over, the three of us were enjoying refreshments in the lobby when a dark-haired young woman approached us. Chris introduced her as Jenny and said she was also a member of the society. I sensed that Jenny was going to play an important role in my son's life, and some of his attention would shift from me to her—as it should.

Had George helped Chris resolve a dependency issue that had gone on for too long? I couldn't say.

The interventions Chris had tried thus far hadn't cured him, but I believe that most of them—including George's color therapy and Pier Rubesa's Bioscope—strengthened him in subtle ways. Certainly, I had no reason to believe that they had caused him any harm.

Chapter 48

❋ Changes

CHRIS TURNED TWENTY-NINE in 2013. He was able to express himself more clearly, making communication with others easier. Through the operatic society, he was developing new friendships, and he was spending much of his free time with Jenny. Jenny was patient and kind. I never heard her patronize Chris or correct his unusual logic. How could he fail to blossom when people treated him with respect?

That summer, Chris flew to England to take a one-week course in directing stage productions. In the fall, he took a bold step and enrolled in a French-language acting class that met every Monday night from September to May. He never missed a single class and could now add acting to his résumé.

I was pleased to learn that one of the themes for the class was "Creating a Stage Presence." I envisioned an enormous marquee with flashing lights:

Christopher Forbes, Starring in and Directing His Own Show

I'd been the overly involved stage manager-mother for the past ten years. I was ready to sit back and watch Chris's life take off. His brothers were slowly finding their way. Alex had been living at home off and on for several years while he worked at a bank. Taylor was working in Basel as a web designer and frequently occupied our guest room. While I loved seeing all my sons on a regular basis, I'd recently retired, and I wanted to focus on my book.

Chris also wanted space, but he still wasn't ready for independent living. He was clearly frustrated by living at home, but he's a homebody by nature, and even after all the energy therapies he has experienced, his physical energy is still low. For whatever reason, he lacked the initiative to strike out on his own.

I wasn't the only one who was unhappy about Chris's lack of motivation. Chris's OT complained that he was sabotaging his chances of success. He was often late for appointments, if he showed up at all.

When Chris was thirty-one, he and the OT settled on a plan: Chris would enroll in a sound engineering program. Given Chris's interests and background, this plan made sense. Ian and I had our doubts about whether being a sound engineer was Chris's best career path, but we were willing to support anything that would help him make better use of his time and give him a skill that might become a source of income and self-esteem.

To help him withstand the rigors of the program, Chris went to see a homeopath that he found in the phone book. Homeopathy works at the conscious and subconscious levels to bolster the life force. Homeopathic remedies are based on the principle that like cures like, meaning that a substance taken in small doses will provoke a healing response, whereas the same substance taken in a larger dose would cause symptoms to manifest.[1]

Chris returned home with a vial of phosphorous. After reading about this remedy online, I knocked on Chris's door.

"The homeopath figured you out on your first appointment," I said when Chris opened the door. "You are like phosphorous!"

He allowed me to enter his room, so I perched myself on the end of his bed and read from my notes:

Phosphorous types are characteristically pale and often blond. They like to please people and are so emotionally sensitive to others that they often inappropriately cross boundaries in an effort to be helpful. Similarly, others cross their boundaries until they learn how to say no. They attempt to avoid conflict and confrontation in an effort to keep the peace. They dislike being alone and can be overly attached to home and family. Easily exhausted, both mentally and physically, they need to honor their own limits.

"Is that you or is that you!" I said, putting down my notes.

"I don't know," Chris said, irritated. "Is there anything good about phosphorous?"

I picked up my notes and continued reading. "Highly likable; poetry-loving romantics; infectious smile. They love to sing. Oh, and get this: They often have strikingly red lips!" I looked up and said, "This was something I noticed about you when you were born."

Chris was unimpressed at first, but soon he was grinning. (Having a sunny disposition is a phosphorous trait.)

"And then there's this: 'They are so light and airy they appear to float.' I'm amazed at how well this description fits you!"

Chris saw the homeopath once a month for the next couple of years. (Phosphorous, in various strengths, was the main remedy he was given, though other remedies were occasionally used instead.) During that time, he started voicing his complaints about living at home and not having a job or a degree. His inability to move forward only added to his frustration, but his tendency to give up on his goals if he encountered an obstacle he wasn't equipped to handle contributed to the problem. (If he couldn't find the room where a class was meeting, he simply went home.) Not surprisingly, he dropped out of the sound engineering program after a year.

Soon after, in September 2016, Chris developed motor tics. The tics began innocuously—a bit of a shoulder twist now and then. Doctor Stern (and the homeopath) believed anxiety was at the root of Chris's troubles, most likely resulting from his uncertainty about the future. Doctor Stern thought the symptoms would disappear of their own accord when Chris felt more confident and his situation was more stable.

Changes were in process. Ian and I were talking about making a move to the United States after he retired in 2018. (Ian is American by birth.) We decided to buy a home on Florida's Gulf Coast. (Our idea of the good life!) Chris would come with us. (As a citizen of the United States, Canada, and Switzerland, he'll have a lot of options if he dislikes Margaritaville.) Doctor Stern not only supported Chris's move to the U.S., she was the one who first suggested it, believing that Chris needs to be near family.

If Chris had reservations about moving to Florida, he didn't share them. He would be leaving behind the relationships he had culti-vated—with Doctor Stern, with Jenny, and other friends from the operatic society. ("I've spent so much time with Doctor Stern in the last few years, I'm sure we must have been married in a previous life," Chris told me.)

However, staying in Switzerland wasn't a realistic option for him. His brothers were leaving Geneva, and Chris wasn't ready to live independently. Alex would be starting a graduate program in Dublin in September of 2017, and Taylor was job-hunting in Europe and the United States.

I hoped that Doctor Stern and the homeopath were right about Chris's tics being caused by anxiety, but I was concerned that Chris might be showing the early signs of a more serious illness, such as TD, Lyme disease, or even Parkinson's. Doctor Stern dismissed my assess-ment; she didn't think the low doses of medications Chris had taken would produce TD, and she doubted he had Lyme disease. (For the past couple of years, Chris had been taking a portion of his 5 mg tablet of Abilify every second day or so.) Nonetheless, Doctor Stern arranged for Chris to see a neurologist to rule out a possible neurological condition.

The neurologist asked Chris a few questions to evaluate his cognitive functioning. After checking Chris's reflexes and having him perform some motor tasks, the neurologist pronounced him "well"—but still "schizophrenic." I couldn't help but wonder, if the doctor hadn't known about my son's history, would he have come up with this diagnosis on his own, based on Chris's presenting symptoms?

Over the next few months, Chris developed a lopsided gait, and, most distressing of all, his eyes started to roll back in their sockets. Some days were better than others, but these symptoms threw Ian and me into a panic. We tried to disregard them as best we could, but I believed, as I always had, that Chris needed to be off all drugs, and I wanted the Abilify stopped—now.

Fortunately, Doctor Stern and Ian agreed, and in February 2017, Chris stopped taking Abilify. He was, once again, drug-free. By May, however, Chris's symptoms were increasing in frequency. Doctor Stern referred him to the neurologist again.

This time, the doctor did not perform any tests or examination, Chris told me afterward; they talked the entire time. (The appointment lasted about an hour.) Chris's motor tics were absent, so the neurologist had nothing to evaluate. The doctor did not think Chris had TD, but he did think he should resume the Abilify.

Chris had no symptoms of psychosis, so why put him on an antipsychotic drug? An older and wiser mother at this stage of the journey, I know now that a medical professional who has been schooled in mainstream views will, more often than not, hold the opinion that a person who has been diagnosed as schizophrenic needs to be on medication—for life.

With my fears about a serious illness assuaged, I came to agree with Doctor Stern's assessment of an anxiety disorder.

When Chris, Ian, and I last met with her, in the summer of 2017, Doctor Stern referred to Chris's schizophrenia in the past tense. She saw no need for Chris to resume taking Abilify.

So far, he's doing okay without it. The motor tics have decreased but not disappeared. At thirty-three, Chris is an empath, an intellectual, a humanitarian; he has something to contribute to the world. But a "schizophrenic," he is not.

He'll have to navigate his own course from here on out. I'll be on the sidelines, cheering for him, whatever he chooses to do with his life.

Maybe he'll finally get a driver's license.

NOTES

CHAPTER 1: Cosmic Concerns

1. Albert Hofmann, the Swiss chemist who first synthesized the mind-altering chemical compound lysergic acid diethylamide (LSD), decided to study chemistry because of "mystical experiences" he'd had in his childhood. He believed the field of chemistry might afford him insights into the essence of the material world. See Albert Hofmann, "LSD: Completely Personal" (speech delivered to the 1996 Worlds of Consciousness Conference in Heidelberg, Germany), *Newsletter of the Multidisciplinary Association for Psychedelic Studies* 6, no. 3 (1996), MAPS/Multidisciplinary Association for Psychedelic Studies website, www.maps.org/news-letters/v06n3/06346hof.html

2. See the introduction (Chapter 1) to *The Prefrontal Cortex* by Joaquín M. Fuster, MD, PhD, for an overview of the prefrontal cortex.

3. John Nash received the Nobel Prize in Economics in 1994 for his contributions to game theory, notably the "Nash equilibrium."

CHAPTER 4: The Hero's Journey

1. Joseph Campbell, *The Hero with a Thousand Faces*, 3rd ed., in *The Collected Works of Joseph Campbell* (Novato, CA: New World Library, 2008).

2. Campbell, *Hero*, 333.

3. Joseph Campbell, *Myths to Live By* (New York: Arkana, 1993), 202.

CHAPTER 10: Things Fall Apart

1. Undated correspondence.

CHAPTER 13: Start with Childhood

1. Infant Feeding Action Coalition (INFACT Canada), "The Only Food Group Baby Needs," *INFACT Newsletter* (Summer 1996), INFACT Canada website, infactcanada.ca/foodgrup.htm

2. I did take Chris to an allergist one summer when he was about four because his face was so swollen that his eyes were almost shut. By the time we saw the doctor, the swelling had disappeared. Lab tests showed that Chris was allergic to dust.

CHAPTER 15: If Psychiatrists Ruled the World

1. See, e.g., the "Become a Member" page on the website of the National Alliance on Mental Illness Greater Orlando (NAMIGO) organization, namigo.org/join/

2. NAMI Genesee County, "Schizophrenia," National Alliance on Mental Illness Genesee County website, www.namigenesee.org/mental-illness/schizophrenia

3. Tardive dyskinesia is a neurological syndrome that sometimes accompanies long-term use of neuroleptic drugs; it is characterized by repetitive and involuntary movements (such as arms and legs) and may include lip smacking and facial grimacing. See National Institute of Neurological Disorders and Stroke, "Tardive Dyskinesia Information Page," National Institutes of Health website, http://www.ninds.nih.gov/disorders/tardive/tardive.htm

CHAPTER 16: Orthomolecular Medicine and Beyond

1. Kallie P. Miller, "Schizophrenia: Introduction," Optimal Life Center website, www.4optimallife.com/schizophrenia-introduction/

2. For information about orthomolecular medicine, visit the Integrated Orthomolecular Network website, https://.ionhealth.ca

3. Abram Hoffer, MD, PhD, and Humphry Osmond, MD, "The Adrenochrome Hypothesis and Psychiatry," *Journal of Orthomolecular Medicine* 14, no. 1 (1999): 49–62. Available online at: http://orthomolecular. org/library/jom/1999/pdf/1999-v14n01-p049.pdf

Hoffer and Osmond were building on the earlier work of Osmond and Smythies, who had discovered that mescaline produced an experience similar to schizophrenia. See Hoffer and Osmond, "Adrenochrome Hypothesis," 49.

4. Hoffer and Osmond, "Adrenochrome Hypothesis," 50.

5. Ibid., 53.

6. Abram Hoffer, MD, PhD, and Humphry Osmond, MRCS, DPM, *How to Live with Schizophrenia*, rev. ed. (New York: Citadel Press, 1992), Authors' Preface.

In *Orthomolecular Treatment for Schizophrenia*, Hoffer describes the problem of relying on tranquilizers as the primary form of treatment as a "Catch-22"; as patients return to normal (clinically and biochemically), they become psychotic from the drugs.

Hoffer asserts that two different psychoses are active—the initial schizophrenic psychosis and the tranquilizer-induced (or iatrogenic) psychosis. Psychiatrists attempt to restore the patient to a normal state by decreasing dosages or trying new drugs. "But since the disease process is still active, when the drug dose is reduced too far, the original schizophrenia-induced psychosis returns. Patients deal with this problem by refusing to take the medication, preferring to be ill with their original psychosis rather than having to suffer the ravages of the iatrogenic psychosis. Thus, patients tend to flip back and forth between these two psychoses. Orthomolecular psychiatry gives them a third and appropriate choice—to become well." Abram Hoffer, MD, PhD, *Orthomolecular Treatment for Schizophrenia* (New Canaan, CT: Keats Publishing, 1999), 34–35. (This material is reproduced with the permission of McGraw-Hill Education.)

7. The basic Hoffer–Osmond protocol consisted of vitamins B_3 (niacin or niacinamide), B_1, B_6, B_{12}, and vitamin C (ascorbic acid).

8. We substituted a B complex tablet for B_1, B_6, and B_{12}.

9. This book was cowritten with Morton Walker, DPM.

10. See "What's at Stake in Nutrition Education during Med School," *AMA Wire*, July 23, 2015, https://wire.ama-assn.org/education/whats-stake-nutrition-education-during-med-school

CHAPTER 17: Doctor Erika

1. See "Energy Medicine: An Overview," a background paper prepared for the National Center for Complementary and Alternative Medicine (now the National Center for Complementary and Integrative Health). This paper is available online at brainline.org, www.brainline.org/article/biofield-therapy-and-energy-medicine-overview

2. Ibid.

3. This fungus is normally found in the body, but a number of factors can cause an imbalance, among them weakened immunity, poor digestion, a diet high in foods that tend to foster the growth of yeast, and the use of antibiotics, which kill off essential bacteria that help maintain the proper balance of flora in the intestines. Candidiasis can be a lifelong problem, Doctor Erika said in her report. In the gastrointestinal tract, it interferes with digestion and nutrient absorption, which in turn affects physical and mental health. Nutritional deficiencies further contribute to intestinal dysfunction and candidiasis, producing a feedback loop that can negatively impact mental health.

4. See Chapter 18 for more on EFT (Emotional Freedom Technique) and energy medicine.

CHAPTER 18: Energy Medicine and Vibrational Energy

1. Chris submitted a petition for reinstatement several years later and the appeal board approved it.

2. In traditional Chinese medicine, the meridians form a network through which energy ("qi") and fluids are distributed throughout the body.

3. Chakras are often described as spinning wheels of energy. The seven commonly recognized chakras are associated with various endocrine glands. The chakras are believed to collect life force energy and distribute it throughout the body through the nervous system. The state of our chakras can influence us physically, emotionally, psychologically, and spiritually.

4. This is the variation that was suggested by Doctor Erika. Many variations have appeared since EFT was first developed, and practitioners have their own preferences, which are reflected in the instructions they give their clients.

5. If the affirmation being used is: "Even though I have an underlying enzyme deficiency associated with my vulnerability to stressors, I deeply and completely love, accept, and forgive myself and all others, and I want my underlying enzyme deficiency to be completely and permanently cured," then the reminder phrase might be: "my remaining enzyme deficiency." The word "remaining" is used after completing one round of EFT while focusing on the problem.

6. Gary Craig was one of the early proponents of EFT.

CHAPTER 19: Clashing Paradigms

1. Hoffer and Osmond, *How to Live with Schizophrenia*, 44–45. (The authors also use the term "flat affect" to describe apathy.)

CHAPTER 20: The Never-Ending Battle

1. The Clinical Antipsychotic Trials of Intervention Effectiveness (CATIE) Project included a schizophrenia trial that was conducted to determine long-range effects and usefulness of antipsychotic medications. See "CATIE – Schizophrenia Trial," National Library of Medicine, U.S. National Institutes of Health website, https://clinicaltrials.gov/ct/show/NCT00014001

2. The newer atypical antipsychotics involved (olanzapine, quetiapine, risperidone, clozapine, and ziprasidone) were introduced in the 1990s. Perphenazine has been available since the 1950s. See "NIMH Study to Guide Treatment Choices for Schizophrenia," *ScienceDaily*, September 20, 2005, www.sciencedaily.com/releases/2005/09/050920074954.htm

3. Ibid.

4. See National Institute of Mental Health, "Questions and Answers about the NIMH Clinical Antipsychotic Trials of Intervention Effectiveness Study (CATIE) – Phase 2 Results" (6. Was Perphenazine Included in Phase 2?), National Institutes of Health website, April 1, 2006, https://www.nimh.nih.gov/funding/clinical-research/practical/catie/phase2results.shtml

5. In 2007, I attended the 36th Annual International Conference, "Orthomolecular Medicine Today" in Toronto, sponsored by the International Society for Orthomolecular Medicine (ISOM). Margot Kidder was a workshop presenter.

CHAPTER 21: The Levels of Healing

1. Solian (amisulpride) is manufactured by Sanofi, a French company. As of 2016, amisulpride was not approved by the FDA for use in the United States.

2. "Biography of Dr. Ryke Geerd Hamer," *The German/Germanic New Medicine®* website, www.newmedicine.ca/bio.php

3. Ryke Geerd Hamer, "The Five Biological Laws of the German New Medicine," (presentation, First International Congress on Complementary and Alternative Medical Cancer Treatment, Madrid, Spain, May 14–15,

2005), 4. Citations are to the PDF file found on Hamer's website: www.germannewmedicine.ca/documents/Madrid-2005-en.PDF

4. Hamer, "Five Biological Laws," 6.

5. Ibid., 12.

6. Ibid.

7. Loren Mosher was chief of the Center for the Study of Schizophrenia at the National Institute of Mental Health (NIMH) from 1968 to1980.

8. Jeanette De Wyze, "Still Crazy After All These Years," *San Diego Weekly Reader*, January 9, 2003, 6, www.sandiegoreader.com/news/2003/jan/09/cover-still-crazy-after-all-these-years/?page=6&

9. Ibid.

10. Ibid.

11. See Alon Marcus, *Foundations for Integrative Musculosketal Medicine: An East–West Approach* (Berkeley, CA: North Atlantic Books, 2005), 424.

12. Ronald W. Kay, "Schizophrenia and Season of Birth: Relationship to Geomagnetic Storms," *Schizophrenia Research* 66, no.1 (2004): 7–20.

13. Doctor Erika attended a conference presentation two years later on the role of magnetism in healing.

14. Stephanie Marohn, *The Natural Medicine Guide to Schizophrenia* (Charlottesville, VA: Hampton Roads, 2003).

15. Stephanie Marohn's book provides a good summary of Klinghardt's levels. See "The Five Levels of Healing" in *Natural Medicine Guide*, 112–136.

16. Marohn, *Natural Medicine Guide*, 125–126.

CHAPTER 22: Beyond the Mainstream

1. Randall C. Wyatt, "Thomas Szasz on Freedom and Psychotherapy," *psychotherapy.net*, December, 2000, www.psychotherapy.net/interview/thomas-szasz

2. Ibid.

3. Soteria was in operation from 1971 through 1983. See De Wyze, "Still Crazy," 1.

4. Loren R. Mosher, MD, "Soteria and Other Alternatives to Acute Psychiatric Hospitalization: A Personal and Professional Review," *Journal of Nervous and Mental Disease* 187, no. 3 (1999): 144.

5. Mosher, "Soteria and Other Alternatives," 142.

6. De Wyze, "Still Crazy," 6.

7. Ibid.

8. Andrew McGhie, "A Comparative Study of the Mother–Child Relationship in Schizophrenia II. Psychological Testing," *British Journal of Medical Psychology* 34, nos. 3–4 (1961): 209–221.

9. Ibid., 217.

CHAPTER 23: The World is a Stage

1. See R. D. Laing, *The Divided Self* (New York: Penguin, 1990), 164.

CHAPTER 24: Expressing Emotion

1. G.W. Brown et al., "Influence of Family Life on the Course of Schizophrenic Illness," *British Journal of Preventive & Social Medicine* 16, no. 2 (1962): 55–68. Available online at: https://www.ncbi.nlm.nih.gov/pmc/articles/PMC1058855/

CHAPTER 25: The Assemblage Point

1. Carlos Castaneda's popular books about the teachings of the Yaqui shaman ("man of knowledge") don Juan Matus read like a modern fable. In *The Fire from Within*, he discusses the assemblage point at length.

2. Angela Blaen, *From Intention to Technology: Assemblage Point and Gemstone Healing* (Crediton, England: The Assemblage Point Centre, Ltd., 2008), 17.

3. Blaen, *From Intention to Technology*, 11–12.
   A high-left assemblage point can indicate problems with fantasies, hallucinations, delirium, and drug abuse. See Blaen, 31.
   The schizophrenia assemblage points are often found equidistant from the center, in high-left and high-right positions, front and back. Sometimes a low-right point is also found. Blaen, 70.

4. Blaen, *From Intention to Technology*, 13.

5. Ibid., 84–85.

6. Carlos Castaneda, *The Fire from Within* (New York: Simon & Schuster, 1984; reprint, Pocket Books, 1991), 110.

7. See, e.g., Jon Whale, *The Catalyst of Power: The Assemblage Point of Man*, 2nd ed. (Eastbourne, England: DragonRising Publishing 2006), 83. PDF e-book.

8. Doctor Blaen recommended a follow-up visit ten days after the first appointment.

CHAPTER 26: A Shift in Awareness

1. Ezek. 1:16, 1:28.

2. The wand is used to stabilize the assemblage point after it is shifted into position.

3. Only the United States and New Zealand allow direct-to-consumer advertising by pharmaceutical companies that includes product claims. US National Library of Medicine, National Institutes of Health, C. Lee Ventola, MS, "Direct-to-Consumer Pharmaceutical Advertising: Therapeutic or Toxic?" *Pharmacy and Therapeutics* 36, no. 10 (2011): 669–684. Available online at https://www.ncbi.nlm.nih.gov/pmc/articles/PMC3278148/

CHAPTER 27: Hearing Voices

1. Intervoice, "What is the Hearing Voices Movement?," The International Hearing Voices Project (Intervoice) website, "About Us" page, www.intervoiceonline.org/about-intervoice

2. A. Hoffer, M.D., Ph.D., "The Adrenochrome Hypothesis of Schizophrenia Revisited," *Journal of Orthomolecular Medicine* 10, no. 2 (1981): 111. This article is available online at www.orthomolecular.org/library/jom/1981/pdf/1981-v10n02-p098.pdf

CHAPTER 28: Fleeting-Improvised Men

1. Daniel Paul Schreber, *Memoirs of My Nervous Illness* (1903), trans. Ida Macalpine and Richard A. Hunter (New York: New York Review of Books, 2000), 28.

2. Francesca Sacco, "Genève: Eldorado des psys," *GHI*, May 21, 2014, www.ghi.ch/le-journal/la-une/geneve-eldorado-des-psys-0
   (Translated into English from French, the first paragraph reads: "Geneva's concentration of all categories of 'soul doctors' (psychiatrists, psychologists, psychotherapists and psychoanalysts) is one of the highest in the world. More than 400 psychiatrists are in private practice or in public institutions. Add to this number 190 psychotherapists and 400 clinical psychologists – plus countless practitioners who offer unconventional approaches. While the Swiss average is 4.3 psychiatrists for 10,000 population, Geneva's is 20.")

3. When converted to other currencies using representative exchange rates from June 2006, the amount would equal:

276,058 USD
149,676 GBP
219,198 EURO
310,013 CAD
374,478 AUD
12,748,121 INR

CHAPTER 29: Family Constellations

1. Doctor Klinghardt uses Family Constellation work for healing the intuitive body (level 4). See Marohn, *Natural Medicine Guide*, 119.

2. See Marohn, *Natural Medicine Guide*, 119–123.

3. Ibid.

CHAPTER 33: The Alexander Technique

1. See Marohn, "Restoring the Tempo of Health: Cranial Osteopathy" in *Natural Medicine Guide*, 137–151.

2. See John Upledger, DO, OMM, "CranioSacral Therapy vs. Cranial Osteopathy: Differences Divide," *Massage Today* 2, no. 10, October 2002, 22. Available online at www.massagetoday.com/mpacms/mt/article.php?id=10571

3. Ibid. According to Upledger, a major difference between the two approaches is in the "quality of touch."

4. For more information on the Alexander Technique, see Michael J. Gelb, *Body Learning: An Introduction to the Alexander Technique*, 2nd ed. (New York: Henry Holt & Co., 1996).

5. F.M. Alexander, *The Use of the Self* (London: Orion, 1985), 82.

CHAPTER 35: More Twists in the Road

1. M. Scott Peck, M.D., *In Search of Stones: A Pilgrimage of Faith, Reason, and Discovery* (New York: Hyperion, 1995), 9.

CHAPTER 39: Time and Space

1. David Healy, a psychiatrist as well as a pharmacologist, argued in a 2012 blog post that greater discernment is needed among doctors about the use of medication. As targets of marketing by pharmaceutical companies, doctors need to learn how to say "No."

Recent estimates suggest companies spend over $50,000 per annum on marketing to each and every doctor in the United States — possibly considerably over $50,000. Despite this, there is not a single medical course on earth that teaches doctors about pharmaceutical company marketing.

Has this marketing done anything to erode the skepticism of doctors? In 1960 doctors rarely had patients on more than one drug at a time and the drugs that were used were for the most part only used for a limited course. Until the early 1990s, the recommendations for antidepressants were for a three-month course, now patients are told they are like insulin and will have to be consumed for life.

David Healy, MD, FRCPsych, "Pharmacosis: So Long and Thanks for All the Fish," *David's Blog*, June 28, 2012, https://davidhealy.org/pharmacosis-so-long-and-thanks-for-all-the-fish/

2. This outcome was found to be associated with the patients' internal characteristics, including greater resilience. See Martin Harrow and Thomas H. Jobe, "Factors Involved in Outcome and Recovery in Schizophrenia Patients Not on Antipsychotic Medications: A 15-Year Multifollow-Up Study," *Journal of Nervous and Mental Disease* 195, no. 5 (2007): 406–414. Available online at https://www.ncbi.nlm.nih.gov/pubmed/17502806

3. Ibid.

4. See Claudia Dreifus, "Using Imaging to Look at Changes in the Brain," *New York Times*, September 15, 2008, www.nytimes.com/2008/09/16/health/research/16conv.html

Doctor Andreasen is a widely respected neuroscientist. She and her team at the University of Iowa have demonstrated that antipsychotic drugs have a "subtle but measurable" influence on brain tissue loss. See Beng-Choon Ho, MRCPsych et al., "Long-term Antipsychotic Treatment and Brain Volumes: A Longitudinal Study of First-Episode Schizophrenia," *Archives of General Psychiatry* 69, no. 2 (2011): 128–137. (Two hundred eleven patients diagnosed with schizophrenia or schizoaffective disorder who were part of the Iowa Longitudinal Study underwent neuroimaging brain scans. Choices about drugs and dosages were made by treating psychiatrists, not the researchers. All three classes of antipsychotic drugs (typical, nonclozapine atypical, and clozapine) were associated with decreases in gray matter (GM) volume.)

Available online at jamanetwork.com/journals/jamapsychiatry/fullarticle/211084

The authors note the potential "clinical implications" for the long-term use of antipsychotics (p. 134) as well as the importance of prescribing "the lowest doses necessary to control symptoms" (p. 135).

CHAPTER 40: Hearing and Listening

1. Don Campbell, "Chanting, Listening and the Electronic Ear: The Pioneering Work of Dr. Alfred Tomatis," Sound Healers Association website, www.soundhealersassociation.org/don-campbell-chanting-listening-and-the-electronic-ear

2. See "Listening vs. Hearing" page of The Listening Centre's website, www.listeningcentre.com/why-listening-training/listening-vs-hearing

3. Ibid.

4. Alfred A. Tomatis, *The Conscious Ear: My Life of Transformation through Listening* (Barrytown, NY: Station Hill Press, 1992), 208–209.

5. Don Campbell, *The Mozart Effect: Tapping the Power of Music to Heal the Body, Strengthen the Mind, and Unlock the Creative Spirit* (New York: Avon Books, 1997), 19.

6. Ibid.

7. Tomatis considered Mozart's music (especially the violin concertos) to be the best healer and "a very good mother." Campbell, *The Mozart Effect*, 22.

8. The mother's voice (recorded and filtered) is sometimes used in an individual's sessions (primarily with children).

CHAPTER 41: The Sound Shaman

1. "In the beginning was the Word, and the Word was with God, and the Word was God." John 1:1.

2. The Big Bang Theory posits an inflating (expanding) universe that started from a "singularity." See, e.g., Elizabeth Howell, "What Is the Big Bang Theory?" *Space.com*, June 12, 2017, https://www.space.com/25126-big-bang-theory.html

CHAPTER 43: Lucid Dreams

1. A lucid dream is a dream in which the dreamer is aware that he is in a dream state and can exert some control over the action. For further

information, see B. Alan Wallace, *Dreaming Yourself Awake: Lucid Dreaming and Tibetan Dream Yoga for Insight and Transformation* (Boston, MA: Shambhala, 2012).

CHAPTER 45: Building Rapport

1. See Alice Henkes, "Fredie Beckmans - Truths Told as if They Were Lies," Kunstbulletin (January/February 2013). Available online at: www.artlog. net/en/kunstbulletin-1-2-2013/fredie-beckmans-truths-told-if-they-were-lies

CHAPTER 47: Bioenergetics

1. Two years later, in 2015, researchers at the University of Virginia School of Medicine announced that they had discovered a previously unknown central nervous system lymphatic system. This discovery alters previous assumptions about neuroimmunology and could affect the study of neurological diseases that have an immune component. See Antoine Louveau et al., "Structural and Functional Features of Central Nervous System Lymphatic Vessels," *Nature* 523 (July 16, 2015): 337–341.

CHAPTER 48: Changes

1. For an in-depth look at the history, philosophy, and use of homeopathy, see Amy L. Lansky, *Impossible Cure: The Promise of Homeopathy* (Portola Valley, CA: R.L. Ranch Press, 2003).

BIBLIOGRAPHY

Alexander, F.M. *The Use of the Self.* London: Orion, 1985.

Beckett, Samuel. *Waiting for Godot: A Tragicomedy in Two Acts.* London: Faber & Faber, 1956.

Brown, G.W., E.M. Monck, G.M. Carstairs, and J.K. Wing. "Influence of Family Life on the Course of Schizophrenic Illness." *British Journal of Preventive & Social Medicine* 16, no. 2 (1962): 55–68.

Blaen, Angela. *From Intention to Technology: Assemblage Point and Gemstone Healing.* Crediton, England: The Assemblage Point Centre, Ltd., 2008.

Campbell, Don. *The Mozart Effect: Tapping the Power of Music to Heal the Body, Strengthen the Mind, and Unlock the Creative Spirit.* New York: Avon Books, 1997.

Campbell, Joseph. *The Hero with a Thousand Faces.* 3rd ed. In *The Collected Works of Joseph Campbell.* Bollingen Series XVII. Novato, CA: New World Library, 2008.

———. *Myths to Live By.* New York: Arkana, 1993.

Castaneda, Carlos. *The Fire from Within.* New York: Simon & Schuster, 1984. Reprint, New York: Pocket Books, 1991.

Frederick, Sue. *I See Your Dream Job.* New York: St. Martin's Press, 2009.

Foster, Joaquín M. *The Prefrontal Cortex.* 5th ed. London: Academic Press, 2015.

Gelb, Michael J. *Body Learning: An Introduction to the Alexander Technique.* 2nd ed. New York: Henry Holt & Co., 1996.

Harrow, Martin, and Thomas H. Jobe. "Factors Involved in Outcome and Recovery in Schizophrenia Patients Not on Antipsychotic Medications: A 15-Year Multifollow-Up Study." *Journal of Nervous and Mental Disease* 195, no. 5 (2007): 406–414. doi:10.1097/01.nmd.0000253783.32338.6e.

Hay, Louise. *You Can Heal Your Life.* Carlsbad, CA: Hay House, 1984.

Ho, Beng-Choon, Nancy C. Andreasen, Steven Ziebell, Ronald Pierson, and Vincent Magnotta. "Long-term Antipsychotic Treatment and Brain Volumes: A Longitudinal Study of First-Episode Schizophrenia." *Archives of General Psychiatry* 69, no. 2 (2011): 128–137. doi:10.1001/archgenpsychiatry.2010.199.

Hoffer, A. "The Adrenochrome Hypothesis of Schizophrenia Revisited." *Journal of Orthomolecular Medicine* 10, no. 2 (1981): 98–118.

Hoffer, Abram. *Orthomolecular Treatment for Schizophrenia.* New Canaan, CT: Keats Publishing, 1999.

Hoffer, Abram, and Humphry Osmond. "The Adrenochrome Hypothesis and Psychiatry." *Journal of Orthomolecular Medicine* 14, no. 1 (1999): 49–62.

———. *How to Live with Schizophrenia.* Rev. ed. New York: Citadel Press, 1992.

Hoffer, Abram, and Morton Walker. *Smart Nutrients: Prevent and Treat Alzheimer's and Senility, Enhance Brain Function and Longevity.* 2nd rev. ed. Ridgefield, CT: Vital Health Publishing, 2002.

Kay, Ronald W. "Schizophrenia and Season of Birth: Relationship to Geomagnetic Storms." *Schizophrenia Research* 66, no.1 (2004): 7–20. doi:10.1016/S0920-9964(02)00495-4.

Laing, R. D. *The Divided Self.* New York: Penguin, 1990.

Lansky, Amy L. *Impossible Cure: The Promise of Homeopathy.* Portola Valley, CA: R.L. Ranch Press, 2003.

Louveau, Antoine, Igor Smirnov, Timothy J. Keyes, Jacob D. Eccles, Sherin J. Rouhani, J. David Peske, et al. "Structural and Functional Features of Central Nervous System Lymphatic Vessels." *Nature* 523 (July 16, 2015): 337–341. doi:10.1038/nature14432.

Marcus, Alon. *Foundations for Integrative Musculoskeletal Medicine: An East–West Approach.* Berkeley, CA: North Atlantic Books, 2005.

Marohn, Stephanie. *The Natural Medicine Guide to Schizophrenia.* Charlottesville, VA: Hampton Roads, 2003.

McGhie, Andrew. "A Comparative Study of the Mother–Child Relationship in Schizophrenia II. Psychological Testing." *British Journal of Medical Psychology* 34, nos. 3–4 (1961): 209–221. doi:10.1111/j.2044-8341.1961. tb00946.x.

Menninger, Karl. *Whatever Became of Sin?* 3rd ed. New York: Hawthorn Books, 1975.

Mosher, Loren R. "Soteria and Other Alternatives to Acute Psychiatric Hospitalization: A Personal and Professional Review." *Journal of Nervous and Mental Disease* 187 (1999): 142–149.

Peck, M. Scott. *In Search of Stones: A Pilgrimage of Faith, Reason, and Discovery.* New York: Hyperion, 1995.

Schiff, Jacqui Lee, with Beth Day. *All My Children.* New York: Pyramid Books (by arrangement with M. Evans and Co.), 1972.

Schreber, Daniel Paul. *Memoirs of My Nervous Illness.* Published in German in 1903. Translated by Ida Macalpine and Richard A. Hunter. Harvard University Press, 1955. Reprint with introduction by Rosemary Dinnage, New York: New York Review of Books, 2000.

Tomatis, Alfred A. *The Conscious Ear: My Life of Transformation through Listening.* Barrytown, NY: Station Hill Press, 1992.

Torrey, E. Fuller. *Surviving Schizophrenia: A Manual for Families, Consumers, and Providers.* 4th ed. New York: HarperCollins, 2001.

Ventola, C. Lee. "Direct-to-Consumer Pharmaceutical Advertising: Therapeutic or Toxic?" *Pharmacy and Therapeutics* 36, no. 10 (2011): 669-684

Wallace, B. Alan. *Dreaming Yourself Awake: Lucid Dreaming and Tibetan Dream Yoga for Insight and Transformation.* Boston, MA: Shambhala, 2012.

Whale, Jon. *The Catalyst of Power: The Assemblage Point of Man,* 2nd ed. Eastbourne, England: DragonRising Publishing, 2006. PDF e-book.

Motion Pictures and Television Shows

A Beautiful Mind. Directed by Ron Howard. Performed by Russell Crowe, Ed Harris, and Jennifer Connelly. Universal Pictures, DreamWorks Pictures, Imagine Entertainment, 2001. Film.

The Lord of the Rings: The Return of the King. Directed by Peter Jackson. Performed by Elijah Wood, Ian McKellen, and Viggo Mortensen. New Line Cinema, WingNut Films, The Saul Zaentz Co., 2003. Film.

Seinfeld. Created by Larry David and Jerry Seinfeld. Performed by Jerry Seinfeld, Julia Louis-Dreyfus, Michael Richards, Jason Alexander. Castle Rock Entertainment, 1989–1998. Television series.

The Simpsons. Created by Matt Groening, James L. Brooks, Sam Simon. Fox Broadcasting Co., 1989– . Television series.

Superman Returns. Directed by Bryan Singer. Performed by Brandon Routh and Kate Bosworth. Warner Bros., Legendary Entertainment, Peters Entertainment, Bad Hat Harry Productions, and DC Comics. 2006. Film.

Tais-toi! (Also titled *Ruby & Quentin.*) Directed by Francis Veber. Performed by Gérard Depardieu and Jean Reno. Union Générale Cinématographique (UGC), DD Productions, EFVE Films, TF1 Films Production, FILMAURO, 2003. Film.

INDEX

ABOUT THE AUTHOR

ROSSA FORBES received a B.A. from Queen's University and an M.B.A. from York University. She lived for many years in Geneva, Switzerland, where she worked for an international organization. She and her husband now live in Florida with their eldest son, who was diagnosed with schizophrenia at the age of twenty.

Made in the USA
Lexington, KY
01 October 2017